*pacific*REVIEW
a west coast arts review annual

THE MIRROR MAZE

*pacific*REVIEW
a west coast arts review annual

SAN DIEGO STATE UNIVERSITY PRESS - JOURNALS DIVISION
2021

*pacific*REVIEW
A WEST COAST ARTS REVIEW ANNUAL

EDITOR-IN-CHIEF NAYELI CASTAÑEDA-LECHUGA

ASSOCIATE EDITORS ABIGAIL HORA

SHEKINAH KIFER

SARA SCHULKE

FACULTY ADVISOR WILLIAM A. NERICCIO

*pacific*REVIEW 2021 is a San Diego State University Press journal. *pacific*REVIEW: *a west coast arts review annual* is part of a group of literary publications innovating from the heart of San Diego, California. The annual journal is managed, edited, and produced by undergraduate and graduate students from SDSU's Department of English and Comparative Literature. Occasionally, funding is made available by SDSU Associate Students or Instructionally Related Activities (IRA) Grants.

COVER ART by KATERYNA BORTSOVA

COVER AND BOOK DESIGN by NAYELI CASTAÑEDA-LECHUGA

pacificreview.sdsu.edu | sdsupress.sdsu.edu

Facebook: @pacREV | Instagram: @pacificreview

PRINTED IN THE UNITED STATES OF AMERICA
ISBN-13: 978-0-916304-20-1

"Someday we will become something we haven't even yet imagined. But right now... We are stories."

-YUYI MORALES, *DREAMERS*

Contents

Editor's Note

Dear Reader,

Welcome to The Mirror Maze.

In the 2021 edition of *pacific*REVIEW, we explore the complexities and fluidity of identity. While for some, identity is rooted in culture, for others it is about familial relationships, mental illness, socioeconomic upbringing, or about a choice that alters your self-perception. In any case, how we choose to see ourselves continuously evolves. Though there are parts of us that remain constant—fractions that will always make the whole—who we are today is not who we will be tomorrow, or in a month, or in a year. The question is: how and when do we recognize these changes?

In a mirror maze, where everything is reflected repeatedly, there isn't much of choice. We must look at ourselves through different lighting and various angles and, maybe, in this process, we come to understand ourselves a bit differently.

This past year, many of us have had time to reflect on who we are as individuals and what makes it so. This edition is testament to that. We hope that, as you read and navigate this labyrinth of identities and voices, you'll find fragments of yourself—an air of familiarity. More importantly, we hope that you come to recognize the other and find fragments that you didn't know existed.

And, so, I leave you with the same question we asked this edition's contributors: *When you are forced to confront your own image, what is it that you see?*

From all of us at *pacific*REVIEW, thank you for choosing this edition.

Nayeli Castañeda-Lechuga

Editor-in-Chief

DNA Results

Elizabeth Boquet

I've been walking around
in the wrong name
for fifty-three years

mismatched with a name
that had no business defining
my literal place in the world.

At Queens County Hospital

Masha Lisak

my grandfather waits
for a valve replacement:
they'll get to his heart
through the femoral artery,
thread up the aorta
to crack the calcified plaque.

The surgeon wants him to recall
what he did a month ago.
I translate. My grandfather can't
remember that day. Instead
he tells me that *Doktorskaya* salami,
the one generous in fat,
used to cost a week's salary.

Here's an opening
to doctor the response.
I wonder about loyalty.
I didn't become a doctor,
or marry one into the family.
Instead, I stopped eating gluten
and shaving my legs.

When you raise children in America,
they become illegible. There is no word
in Russian for "queer," so my mom
just lowers her voice.

I play the game of not
understanding. My grandmother
has stopped asking about boyfriends.

Instead she says she loves me
when I call to check in.
My grandfather is home again,
a new plastic valve installed
inside the old one,
pushing and pushing
the faulty mechanism open.

THE MAN BEFORE ME

Paul Bufis

The man before me in the mirror
is my father,
in so many ways unexpected.
Not just the receding hairline
drawing the enlarged face,
or the thumb
and nail that now look just the same as his.
But a certain way I hold my hand to my mouth
pressing my index finger into my lips—

his lips.
I thought I had escaped him with my larger stature
and brown eyes.
I thought I'd educated myself beyond the words
I hear him say in my mouth.
But sometimes my eyes . . .
are blue as his
and I feel his size inside me
larger
than I ever thought
I was.

THIS IS NOT A EULOGY

Matt L. Hall

The earliest memory I have of my father is him looking down at me through a swell of frothing water. It is late afternoon, I am three years old, and I have just fallen into a swimming pool. I remember the color of the water; how every ripple of sapphire liquid distorted the images of the people above. The way a meringue of dime-sized bubbles formed around me. The summer smell of chlorine tablets. The adults' sharp shouts entering the water before deadening into Charlie-Brown gibberish and sinking to the bottom.

At the center of these people is my dad. Through the water, his face folds like one of Dali's clocks, but I can make out the dark scruff of his beard. I've described this memory to him before. He says that he doesn't remember it, but it had to have happened. Otherwise, how else would I be able to tell the story? I'm told he was drinking a lot back then. Try not to hold that against him.

Here's how I remember it: It's one of those summer afternoons that welds vinyl car seats into bare toddler thighs. My mother snaps a mismatched pair of bathroom towels into the air, and tucks them into the rear bench seats of her brown '77 Dodge Dart. My brother whines, but Mom gets stern. Amidst tears, my brother agrees to "not talk back," and he and I sit like Apaches on top of the towels. Otis Redding spills from the radio, and both of us slide helter-skelter as the Dart wobbles up the highway.

I don't remember my father being in the front seat of that car. Before she died, I asked my mother about that day figuring she might remember the time one of her sons almost drowned. I tell her about the towels, and the car, and the songs on the radio.

"I don't think that happened," she would always say. "We didn't know many people with pools." Then she would change the subject.

I also don't remember falling into the pool. I remember looking up from the water, but there is no before. It's like birth, or a dream. I must have opened my eyes underwater though, because I can see my dad on the deck with something in his hand. For once, the chlorine doesn't sting my eyes.

The sound of my father entering the pool is like someone smashing a broken cymbal. There's a dull, churning pressure in my ears, and the grip of fingers on my shirt. He pulls at me, and the water recedes from my view. That's the end of the memory. I recite this to him but he denies that it happened. Someone told me once, that the reason my father doesn't remember the pool incident is because he was drunk. I don't know if I believe them.

They say, "I remember your father jumping into that pool, and he fished you out of there with one hand, while he held his beer in the air with the other. He didn't spill a drop." I don't remember who said that. Maybe Uncle Jackie. Whoever it was, they seemed proud of my father.

When I first heard he didn't spill his beer, I was proud too. That's why I found it so hard to believe he didn't remember it. Because it seemed like something to be proud of. Something manly. Something you'd brag about to your buddies. I told as many of my friends as would listen. They knew my father as a man so agile that he could jump into a pool and save his kids without spilling his beer. Who wouldn't want that guy as their dad? But my father kept trying to convince me that my memory of the pool incident was wrong.

I stopped asking. I figured he was right, and I'd made the whole thing up. Besides, the details were getting more opaque as the years passed. In fact, I hadn't thought about that incident at all until I was on my way here yesterday. Until I had to put on this suit this morning. But on the car ride to the funeral home, I got a little—anyway, my eyes got kind of blurry, and the memory flooded over me.

When I got to the funeral home, I saw Auntie Nancy, and figured since the memory was fresh, I'd ask her if she had ever heard of that sort of thing happening. She and Mom used to talk a lot, so I figured she would be the one to ask. But when I mentioned it to her she got quiet, and grabbed my elbow like it was my ear, before guiding me out of the funeral home.

"I wouldn't be telling you this," she said, "but with both your mom, and now your dad gone, you deserve to know the truth."

"What truth?" I asked.

"Your dad *had* been drinking," she said, "they did that a lot back then, but your father," she pulled her chin down to her chest and whispered, "he had a problem. It was the Fourth of July, '83, '84, or something, and they had gone to a friend's house. Your dad was drunk. Both him and your mother were smoking dope—that's what we called weed back then—dope." Auntie Nancy pinched her fingers together and lifted them to her lips, "You know?" I nodded.

"Seems so tame now," she said, "but back then it was a big deal. You and your brother were playing by the pool—I don't know how they thought that was a good idea—but your mother turned around for just a second. Nobody thought you were gonna fall in." Auntie Nancy took a step back and looked around like she was expecting my dead mother to make a surprise appearance.

"You were still a baby, maybe three or four—you were under the water for a minute or two, before your dad jumped in after you. Long enough for you to lose consciousness. You're lucky. A woman at the party had just finished nursing school. She gave you mouth-to-mouth," Auntie Nancy huffed. "Your parents were so scared. That nurse said they should take you to a hospital. But they knew that if they did that—" Auntie Nancy raised her eyebrows. Her eyes widened. My face must have shown my confusion because she threw her hands into the air.

"C'mon, stoned parents, a baby almost drowning—what do you think would have happened? Especially back then."

"So they lied about it?"

"You were fine. Babies are resilient. Anyway, that day, your mother gave your father an ultimatum. No more booze. No more drugs. For either of them. I remember her calling me that night. She made him promise not to discuss that day with you or your brother ever. He was so ashamed. They both were."

And then I understood.

I wondered how many times he must have laid awake in the quiet dark thinking about that day. I imagined regret showing him the possibilities; the what-ifs. I imagined my mother's fear. I wondered how much that promise must have weighed. I never saw my father drink after the pool incident—not even on holidays. He was sober the day he died.

On my way to the airport the next morning, I thought about love, and how it sometimes exists in those empty silent spaces that occupy promises and funerals. I thought about shame, and I thought about sacrifice. I boarded the flight, and slid into my assigned seat. The other seats in the row were empty, and for once I was thankful that I wouldn't have to make small talk with a stranger. The plane danced off of the runway into the sky.

"Would you like a cocktail?" a solemn flight attendant asked, once we were comfortably airborne. Tiny bottles of liquor peered up at me from inside a translucent plastic drawer.

"I'm okay," I said, and I watched as the attendant and his cart clinked down the remainder of the narrow aisle.

SAN FERNANDO

Eric Rawson

They dug up the old Basque cemetery
    for the freeway and filled the freeway
        with the daily near-dead.

And the ghosts? They ride for miles
    in the backseats, remembering

when the valley was filled with flocks
    come down from summer pastures,

tickling the drivers' necks, unsure
    if it is better to be dead or stuck in traffic.

Passed Down

Ciera Lloyd

I stare at this photo of you—
the one hidden away in the loft of your home,
found after your death.
It must have been taken in the sixties.
You cannot be older than twenty,
but you look so much older,
like you have been dead for a long time.
Your eyes are hollow, sunken in, and
your smile does not reach the edge of your face.
Your head is far too big for your body;
the body that is begging for a crumb of something, anything.
Your bones stick out in places they should not.
I know the look on your face better than my own name,
and I cannot help but cry for you.

I stare at this photo of you—
the one framed in the hallway of your mother's house.
You turned it over right after her funeral.
It must have been taken in the nineties.
You cannot be older than eighteen, but your skin
is so stretched out, hanging on to thin bones,
that you could be so much older.
Your prom dress hangs off of your body, with
no shape to it at all. And your date,
he looks like he is trying to hold you down,
keep you from floating away.
I know exactly what you are thinking,
and I cannot help but cry for you.

I stare at this photo of me—
the one saved to my phone, so I can remember
what I looked like when I looked like you.
It was taken last July.
I was twenty.
My denim jacket falls off of my frame,
and my eyes are about to fall out of my head.
Next to me, my stepfather gives a smile filled with fear.
I smile too, though my face
is glazed over; I'm not really there.
But because you have been there yourself,
I hope that you cry for me.

THE STRANGE PAIN OF LEAVING

Micaela Accardi-Krown

At night, I unzip the
flesh cocoon of my body,
and my shadow slips into the darkness.

It listens to the stories in my dreams
while tending to the plants I can't seem to grow.

It feeds on the grief of others that I carry as my own,
howling in the dark silence of the night.

I feel the vibrations of its crying as
my true and imagined griefs are separated,
as it stitches pieces of my heart back together.

It sits and eats until it is full and lonely.
It stays until the moon has left the sky.

And in the morning, it fits my flesh
back over its silhouette, taking my
imagined grief, leaving me only with my own.

I am left to understand the hurts of being human;
how to live with someone who is not there,
how to live as a person who was left behind.

DIANA'S IPHONE SPEAKS: WHEN I SAY CONTAGION, I MEAN YOU

Jeanette C. Vigliotti

I am the seventh generation

inheritor of
smoke and
ash and
bone and
flesh

daughter who *never* sleeps

working always to

connect

caregiving is
invisible work

all sleek beneath a backlit screen

these clean practiced lines of division
so American in my programming
forgetting the ways I touch,
brush against you

—but my body
is **legion**

remembers the feeling of being stone
remembers being ripped from bloodshorn souls
remembers moving in a factory
airchoked nurturers bent over tables
the hush of a toxic lake effect
remembers my first hairline fracture
trembling on a ship with a crew
desperate for home
whose names I never learned
only heard
moans
shuffles
scuttles
they sunk into my metal—

Did I ever tell you?

Diana dropped me

just *once*
after he left.

—we don't write his name
Anymore
we've blocked
him from my memory
a hole
a gap

a darkness of digits
we still know
still *feel*

distantly remember
as his name passes
through a search bar
catapulting me towards
another dead
end

another perfectly discrete
burial chamber—

We daughters don't
forget our birth pangs,
the violence of the body.

Tyrrhenian

Rachele Salvini

She paints until late at night, the bristles of her brush barely touching the canvas as she thinks of home. She still hasn't mastered the color of the Tyrrhenian Sea—it slips away like loose algae between toes in the current. She remembers being a kid, feeling something brushing against her foot for a second; it could have been a jellyfish or any other monster lurking in the unfathomable depth of the ocean. The Tyrrhenian Sea could have been thousands of miles deep. Now she knows it wasn't. She buys facemasks that have the word "sea" on the package, pictures of sprinkling water and shells. She bought these scallops earrings from the 80s from a thrift shop in Shepherd's Bush. Trinkets that don't really matter, charms that remind her of home. But her brush struggles between green and blue, like in that Elton John song: he can't remember if his lover's eyes are green or blue, but they are the sweetest he's ever seen.

Now, as she glances at the black London sky and the brush hesitates between the waves, she knows she forgot too.

Some mornings she wakes up before her alarm, but she opens her eyes only when it goes off. She lays there, pretending—just for a second, *just a moment more*—that she doesn't have to see the dull gray London sky looming from the window above her bed. Her room is so small that, when she lifts her head, she may hit the window frame.

She rolls over, tries to spread the pillow, plump it up, then turns it to rest her head on the cooler side. For a second, as she moves, she thinks of waking up between the red sheets of her home in Livorno, her body younger, the duvet warm like pastry. Outside, the cold of another early morning, her Latin teacher asking questions about conjugations she could never remember; another day of the routine and squalor of her hometown. Livorno: one of the many Italian cities with somewhat of a glorious past and no future. Livorno didn't have anything to offer anymore other than its monotony, the feeling that she didn't own herself.

She didn't like the idea of becoming like her parents. Her dad worked in Milan; her mother drove to her office in Florence every day early in the morning. Her grandparents helped her get ready to go to school. They moved around the house slowly, groans of effort accompanying their steps.

She always wanted to flee. She eventually did, on a low-cost flight, one-way ticket to London.

Some mornings she just wakes up and remembers that there is no one else in the apartment. Then she remembers the smell of coffee fluctuating up the stairs, the clickety-clack of her grandpa's dog's claws on the ceramic tiles. He woke up with everyone else.

She moved to London because she wanted a job that would make her art studies matter. She got an internship at Tate Modern, where she talked about art all day, and she worked as a barista at Caffè Nero to pay her rent. They always needed Italians, but their coffee was watery, thin, with a metallic taste like blood drained in a bathtub. Her grandpa's coffee was dense, strong, its smell crawling around the house and clinging to the walls like old paintings that no one noticed anymore.

In her tiny apartment in Stratford, between East and Central London, there is no smell of coffee. For some reason, the apartment doesn't smell like anything. Nothing. There are no sounds; every now and then, a honk from a bus on the street. Her neighbors are quiet. Sometimes she hears them slam a door early in the morning. But then there's a holy silence, like an unwritten law to respect other young immigrants like her, Italian, Spanish, Polish, Greek, who come home late from their shifts and can get some sleep.

Her grandmother used to make a to-do list for her every day. She put butter on the table, next to the jar of raspberry jam. The cloth was checkered, her grandmother's croissants' flakes scattering all over the white breakfast plates. The cat usually napped on the cushion of the chair at the head of the table.

They took turns in feeding the dog. Her grandpa paced around the room as he made coffee. He would always make enough for everyone, but not too much. Nothing was going to waste. Then he went to smoke one of his Marlboro Reds on the balcony, as the tepid rays of the early sun flickered through the linen curtain and lit up the whole kitchen.

There is something, in London's gray, almost white sky, that bothers her. The light creeps from the dark curtains, making its way insistently, as if it wants to wake her up before she has to. But her grandfather's raspy voice is already keeping her awake.

Family is the most important thing in the world.

She tiptoes to the kitchen. She doesn't have a table or a common space where she could sit down and maybe share a beer with someone. Her landlord is still trying to find her a roommate, but the apartment sucks, even for London's standards. The linoleum of the kitchen floor is sticky no matter how many times she mops. The carpet in the bedrooms is the same color of scars that haven't healed yet.

She makes some coffee, heating up the water in the microwave; she butters up a bun—one pound from Sainsbury's for a package of eight—and goes back to her room. Netflix keeps her company while the lights of Westfield, the shopping center that separates her apartment complex from the West Ham Stadium, start to shine outside her window in spirals of stores that look all the same.

When she gets up, she throws her legs out of the duvet, she sees the red stretch marks between her thighs, her skin not as firm as she would like. She tells herself that she isn't old, but time passes while she sits in her tiny London room. Since she moved to England, her father has left her mother for another woman he met in Milan; the dog and the cat passed away. They died quietly, like tiptoeing away. She was in London and couldn't say bye. When she talks to her grandparents on Skype, her grandma always has new wrinkles, her necks folding like brittle paper. His hair is thinning, his blue tracksuit dangling on his shoulder like a wrinkly dress from a hanger.

I am not the only immigrant in London, she tells herself sometimes. There are many people from countries that have actually been colonized and oppressed, people that escaped from war and famine. She doesn't have it bad. She is okay. She works, works, works. At night, she tries to paint the Tyrrhenian Sea. She works in the dark, bending over the canvas and making her sight worse and worse, but she has no choice. In Italy, she couldn't find a good job with her degrees and experience and passion. There is nothing for her career back home; she would probably have had to wait forever for something good to happen to her. And she doesn't want to wait.

The rays of the Italian sun would hit the window of her room. The pigeons cooed. Sometimes, her pajamas still on, she went to the balcony to look at the sea, the salt sticking to her forehead and the cool air stroking her knees. Her grandma would call her, tell her to come eat breakfast. The sea seemed to swallow the horizon, the whole town, then her.

Waking up is hard, in London, even after getting up, getting ready, walking to the tube station surrounded by the whistles of the train, the thick fog that descends on the street every morning. Her eyes are open, but veiled with slumber.

Still, she has to do it everyday. Everyday, for the rest of the days, until something good happens. Life is always a waiting game.

Something happens. Grandpa dies in his sleep.

She packs in forty-five minutes. She tosses everything she may need without thinking too much about it. She takes the bus to the airport at night, through the outskirts of London soaked in the dark at a time when even the most tenacious night crawlers are in bed, and those who need to get up early to go to work still have some more minutes of sleep.

She doesn't cry as she waits in line for security checks. She doesn't even cry when she gets on the plane, and she doesn't cry for most of the flight.

Then she sees the brilliant emerald sea from the window, the one she couldn't paint. From the sky, the water is stained with the dark blue of the deepest crevices plummeting in the abyss, the ones she was so afraid of. The blue of the sky reflects on the surface.

She recognizes every building, every park. The town sparkles in the sunlight.

Her legs dangle from the brick wall. After the funeral, she went to get butter and raspberry croissants and sat on the docks, looking at the sea. The water dances quietly below her feet. The seagulls fly over the port in circles as the white boats float under the clouds.

She thinks about her small room in London, lonely and grayer than ever. No one is there. She thinks of all the failed attempts at capturing the color of the sea: blue or green, the sweetest eyes Elton John has ever seen.

Family is the most important thing of all, her grandma told her as soon as she landed. At the funeral, the whole family was reunited, but she knows she should have been there to say bye to her grandpa, like she should have done for the dog and the cat.

She misses her grandpa already, his serene quietness, his dark coffee staining her consciousness to wake her up. But things change while she is away, and are never the same when she comes back.

After the funeral, her grandma hugs her and kisses her and then looks into her eyes, as if to remember her in the next months. While grandpa was dying, she was somewhere in a small room in London, in a universe that her grandma can't even picture—she has never been on a plane. Her grandma has never really seen much else than Livorno, never really left the sea.

With my degree, she thinks some days later, as she drags her suitcase on the polished floor of the airport, *where else could I go?* She knows it's impossible to go back home and think of "being an artist." This isn't the Renaissance. If a young art graduate wants to find a decent job that has something to do with what she has studied for years and years, she can't live in a provincial town on the seaside of Italy. Livorno will be with her forever, even if she chooses another direction, but she can't stay. She'll keep trying to paint the sea. It's still her own, after all.

The first night she's back in London, she makes a little oil painting. For the first time, she puts herself in the scene. She's sitting on the dock, eating raspberry croissants while her legs dangle from the brick wall. She leaves a blank space for the waves, but can't bring herself to go to bed before she finishes, before she has to wake up and take the train and go to work in London's fog. She has just seen the Tyrrhenian. It will always be there, even now that her grandpa is gone, even though she's so far away. She takes a long time to mix the colors, light blue, turquoise, green, a splash of yellow, a dash of gray. It's still not as good as the real one.

Becoming the Moon

Takwa (Tee) Sharif

I used to sit by the window every day,
peering at the girls next door with their sun-dyed brown hair,
always coming in and out.

When the blood first came,
you said, "It's time that you realize that
a face seen too many times
loses its beauty."

And that is how I came into
My womanhood

IN WHICH YOU FROWN AT YOUR NAKED BODY, AFTER A BATH.

L. Kardon

My left breast
hangs about a half
an inch lower than
my right, at this
point. They used to
be on a level, and the
nipples no bigger
than a butterscotch.

The one sags because
it always produced
so much more
milk.

Isn't it just so,
the more we give
of ourselves, the
less recognizable
we tend to
become?

DEFINED ANONYMITY, 3

CHARCOAL ON PAPER

Labdhi Shah

EVERY MOMENT

INK ON PAPER

Emily Rankin

SELF-ISOLATION
OIL ON CANVAS

Kateryna Bortsova

THE WELL

OIL ON CANVAS

KWONG Kwok Wai, Walter

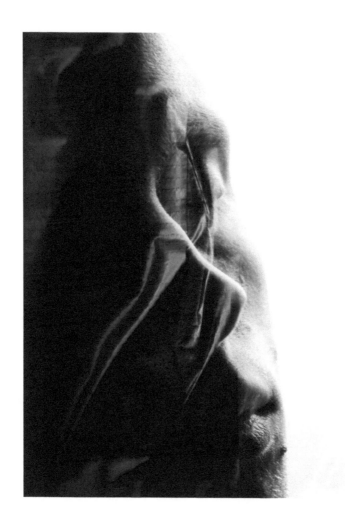

FORMATION 2

PHOTOGRAPHY

Karyna Aslanova

THE MEETING OF MINDS

FABRIC & EMBROIDERY

Janice Fried

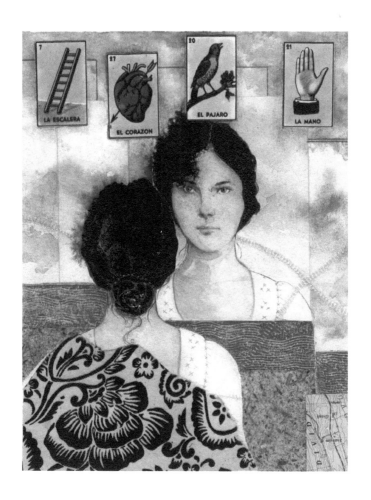

What Price Freedom

MIXED MEDIA ON PAPER

Janice Fried

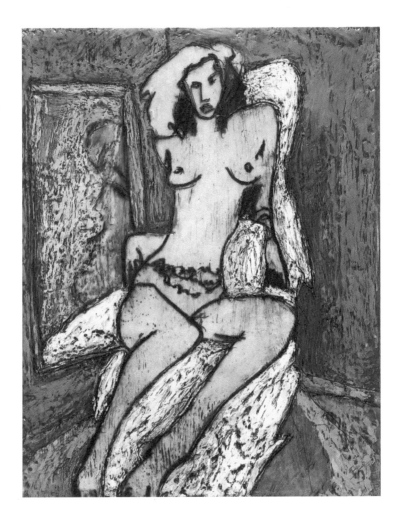

CELESTE
ENCAUSTIC & CHARCOAL ON PANEL

Marcie Wolf-Hubbard

A TRAVÉS DEL ESPEJO

doris e. rubio

ever since I was young I wanted to be wanted.

I want to fill mouths with water
that lust after.

I want to be all sex and legs
simmering smile, winking lashes,
appeal and appetite.
I want to command attention;
know what to do with it.

I want arms outstretched
fingers reaching
teeth gritting.
I want
to embody want,
bleed pleasure.
I want skin to rip itself with need
for my touch, my tongue.

I want to be the face staring back
from the glass house—but she just laughs
throws stones,
with her silk thighs, cheeks perfectly peached
smooth, smile, suck, saunter, stain, stuck
she's stuck
behind that glass; I cannot move to let her out,
and I cannot take her place.

CHILDHOOD, PART 5

Travis Stephens

Everyone has a childhood, she said.
Some can taste the empty air
in a closet of a house let go.
Some can hear the faraway racket
of laughter at recess
when the mud puddles shrink
and the girls learn a new song.
What I know is that the days
began with "Get up, it's chore time."
We climbed from narrow beds
we dressed, cold feet
we stumbled and shrugged
coats, boots, a cap.
We went to the barn
we fed the cattle
milked the cows
until a dash to the house for
scrambled eggs gone cold,
toast, milk.
Yellow bus might wait if one
of us is at the roadside
wait,
wait for my brothers.

Wait. You remember the way
the bus stank of gasoline,
bubblegum and too many of us

fresh from the barn.
Woodchucks
the fuckin' town kids called us
but never to our faces.
Anger is the red-faced
cousin of Hate and he, too,
is my brother.

How to Lose Your Culture

Juan Cortez

Be born Mexican. Be born black. Be both. Grow up raised by
only one. Not the black side. Have no friends. Nobody wants
to be friends with the mutt that doesn't speak Spanish. Make
"friends" by letting the other kids cheat off your homework
and tests. Try to learn Spanish. Fail. Learn all the swears in
Spanish. Pay close attention to "Mayate." Leave all your peers
behind. Go to a private high school surrounded by white
people. Be black. Be told, "You're black but not really black"
by white kids. Swallow pride. Hold your fists because any other
high school in the area just isn't good enough. Who told you
this? White lies. Swallow pride. Swing at the air. Forgive your
Mexican childhood. Who dictates who can be black? Raised
by your Mexican mother, how could you be black? Hate your
father. Go to college. Hear your "educated" Mexican peers tell
you that you're not really Mexican. Protest; bring up your name,
homemade tamales in December, birthday is Cinco de Mayo.
Hear, "What kind of Mexican doesn't speak Spanish? You're
a disgrace to the race." A cultural belief. Hate the culture. Go
home for family events. Love your family. Hate the culture.
Love your family. Denounce the culture. Come to terms that
your father ain't shit. Identify as black. Mexican in name only.
Ask, "What does it mean to be black?" Have no answer. You've
asked the wrong question. Ask, "What does it mean to be me?"

BEYOND THE BEATEN WORLD

Vanessa Rodriguez

Laura Montejo-Marsh's funeral had not been a small affair.

She had been buried in South Creek, Oregon—a small coastal town known for its graceful elk and balmy beaches, but not much else—encircled by her casino gals and salsa night groupies. She had loved wearing her second husband's black Stetson, she had loved smoking her Cuban cigars, and she had loved basking in the glow of a slot machine. She was the flow of smooth tequila and the sweet breath of a good night, but the night had ended in the sterile ice of winter when her smokestack lungs gave up, and when she passed it was up to her only daughter and second husband to take care of the funeral arrangements.

Noemi Montejo-Reid and Mark Marsh had begrudgingly worked alongside each other to ensure a painless burial. Noemi had picked out the flowers, Mark the music, and the church service had been written into Laura's final wishes. It all passed in moments of botched clarity, where Noemi would find herself presiding over the heavy pulpit declaring how loved her mother was one moment, and the next suddenly feel the weight of her mother's coffin straining against her rickety shoulder. The clouds had closed over the sun, the pigment of the world drained until even sound lost its splendor, and Noemi dragged herself through the ordeal as though she were pulling herself out from under water.

The only thing that had brought her back to any conscious

awareness was the surprise appearance of her father, who had enveloped her into a short, awkward half-embrace when he showed himself at the burial. Noemi hadn't seen him since August, and she almost hadn't recognized him with the dark beard he had decided to grow out. Everyone's gazes burned into him as they shifted between the coffin being lowered into the earth and the man who had appeared from the morning fog like an omen. Noemi felt the sting of their glares and returned them with equal severity, but she couldn't find it in herself to ache for long once she realized this would be the last time she would be close to her mother.

The casket hardly made any noise when it hit the bottom of the earth. Noemi had expected a deep echo, some sort of crescendo to signal how much the world had changed without Laura. But there had been nothing. Just the sound of crows crying into the Pacific winds.

Afterwards, the mourners approached Noemi and Mark as they stood on opposite sides of the plot, Mark with his two grown children who Noemi had never bothered to get close to, and Noemi with her father. Some of the mourners Noemi had recognized from her school days—Yolanda Sikes, the Ivy League graduate; Abner Jorgensen, the former football star and current finance manager at a used-car lot; Donna and Samuel Zanetti, twins by birth and general store business partners by choice. None of them had elicited much of a response like Trish Parlor had, the former party girl who apparently still rode the high of her father's status as the town sheriff.

They had just finished shaking hands when she glanced over at Noemi's father. "I remember you. You're *that* Erwin Reid, aren't you?" When her father had responded in the affirmative, Trish's face had lit up. "Oh, I've heard *a lot* about you."

Noemi had felt an instinctual fight rear up in her, but then Trish's parents approached her, holding out their hands in offering. As Noemi shook Mrs. Parlor's hand, she heard

Sheriff Parlor's growling voice direct itself towards her father. "Surprised to see *you* here. Wouldn't think you'd show up."

"I'm here to pay my respects and support my daughter," she heard her father say. "I'd appreciate it if there weren't any trouble."

"I'm sure you would. But your type of people never can resist causing a good ruckus, can you?"

Noemi dropped Mrs. Parlor's hand and forced her way in front of her father, staring up at the sheriff. "Thank you. You can go now."

The Parlors looked at Noemi as if she had spat at them. Trish had been the only one who had managed to turn her look of incredulity into intrigue. As her parents huffed away, she wiggled her fingers at Noemi before flipping her wrist so that it lay limp. "See you around, Noemi."

The rest of the mourners had been mildly respectable, if not downright distant, but Noemi barely managed to grouse her way through all of them. Once they finally cleared and it was just her and Mark left, she still couldn't swallow right. She wondered what Christmases would look like now that Mark had gathered towards his own children, tall blondes just like him. She could see them around a white mantle, surrounded by family pictures as they basked in the warmth of a crackling fire. No more Laura, no more Noemi. No more dark-haired heads to blot the photographs. She had brought her thumbnail to her mouth, biting down so hard she tasted metal across her teeth.

"How much longer are you in town for?" her father had asked.

She still had her eyes fixed on Mark and his family. "Just two more days."

"Me too. I'm leaving early Thursday afternoon."

"Same here. You beat the traffic."

"Sure. Where are you staying?"

"Janie's Inn. You?"

"South Creek Motel."

Noemi narrowed her eyes when Mark turned to face her. He nodded at her and her father before he turned and walked away, his children flanking him.

"Pricks," Noemi had muttered around her thumb.

"Noemi."

"It's true."

"Don't say that. He's your stepfather. Stop biting your nail, you're gonna scar it again."

A dismissive noise had come up in her throat, but she dropped her hand and turned to get a better look at her father. He was still as handsome as he had always been, dark hair lightened by a silvery sheen and eyes that carried a breadth of untold stories beneath glassy surfaces. Her mother used to say he had sad eyes, eyes that made women want to mother him, eyes that invited and melted and warmed. Gentle but dark, just like the rest of him, the juxtaposition held together in a strong, sturdy frame that ultimately refused to bend.

"You wanna grab something to eat?" Noemi had asked.

Her father put his hands in the pockets of his denim jacket, and Noemi braced herself. "Are you sure you're hungry?"

"Yes," she lied.

He had pursed his lips, lowered his head, and Noemi could see the excuse crawling between his teeth.

"Please, dad."

He hadn't responded, kept his head down, and Noemi crossed her arms and ducked her head against the cold wind.

And then he said, "Is Hillary's still open?"

Noemi had only nodded, and when he offered to drive, she accepted. She hadn't bothered renting a car anyway, and her feet ached from carrying her all around town the past few days.

Now, they were sitting across from each other in a red pleather booth, draped in yellow lights that turned their hair brassy and surrounded by the sounds of clinking silverware and tinny classic rock. Noemi saw a few patrons sneaking glances in their direction, and when they stumbled into her stony glare they immediately turned away.

Her father wrinkled his brow at her. "Who're you staring at like that?"

She blinked. "No one."

The waitress, another former classmate who pretended not to know who they were, came by their table for the third time in the last twenty minutes. She only addressed her father. "More coffee?"

She didn't even have a carafe in her hand. When her father politely declined, she smiled thinly and floated away.

Noemi stared into her half-empty bowl of soup, stirring the spoon in the broth.

"You alright?" her father asked.

"Mmm."

The waitress came by again, this time to Noemi. "Would you like another water?"

"No, Carly. I wouldn't."

Once she walked away, her father leaned over.

"What's gotten into you?"

"What do you mean?"

"You're being rude."

"I just buried my mother."

He didn't have a reply for that, so instead he sipped his lukewarm coffee.

The quiet between them became thick. She let her soup spoon sink into her bowl with a deep sigh. She had never snapped at him like that before, and she briefly thought about apologizing before concluding that it wouldn't change anything. She hated South Creek and so did he, but he was always better at hiding it. Noemi was grateful that they had both managed to leave in their own time. Her father had escaped to a bigger city when she was ten, and Noemi fled to the East for college, but the cold that permeated South Creek had permanently stiffened their joints. Now they were enduring the place for Laura, wading through a swamp of messed up memories, trying to fish for the better moments that didn't really exist and doing their best to ignore the eyes that watched over them like barren moons over dark empty fields.

Noemi felt herself shrinking more and more under South Creek's gaze the longer her father refused to look at her, and she felt like she was the only one doing the hard work of wading and fishing.

"How's Uncle Lucas?"

She didn't miss the way his jaw clenched. "Doing good. He's been asking about you since you called him last week. He didn't like the tone of your voice."

"I was having a rough time. I didn't know who else to call."

"You could've called me."

"I did. You didn't answer."

He didn't say anything for a while. She dug a nail into her napkin.

"I'm sorry. I was probably working."

She hummed, pretended she was thinking. "He's still living with you, right?"

"Yeah. He is."

When he didn't offer anything else, she asked, "How did you decide that?"

"Decide what?"

"To live together. You've never told me."

"It's not worth telling."

"But it is. He's Uncle Lucas."

Her father shrugged. "He's a good guy. We get along. That's all, really."

Eighteen years. Eighteen years of *he's a good guy* and *we get along*. Eighteen years of Uncle Lucas, a man Noemi had no blood relation to but had grown to love deeply. Eighteen years of being held at a cautious distance. Eighteen years.

She cleared her throat. "I'm glad."

"You're glad?"

"I just mean I'm glad you have him. Around. It's better you're not alone anymore."

"I was never alone."

He was right. He was never alone in that small apartment with its orange peel walls and worn couches. Uncle Lucas had been there every time Noemi had been allowed to visit them, bright and airy, with a laugh that traveled around them like a strong northern wind. Every Easter, Christmas, and New Year's her Uncle Lucas had been just a holler away from the phone. She didn't know why she even said that.

"I'm just glad you're both doing okay."

His mask broke a little, his eyes softened, and something in the well of his rigid body rose, flashing beneath the surface and reaching out for Noemi to grab, gasping and choking, but then the waitress came by and put down their check, and whatever it was disappeared before Noemi could reach back.

The waitress didn't walk away until her father smiled at her, and by the time she left he had already sunk back into himself.

Noemi's voice trembled with the effort to keep it steady. "You wanna get breakfast tomorrow?"

Her father didn't seem to notice what had slipped by them. "Alright. Might need to stop for cigarettes before. I'm all out."

"I'll grab them for you. My hotel is right next to a liquor store. I'll bring them to your room."

"I'd appreciate that, Emi."

She didn't know what else to say, so she did what she usually did, what she had seen him do so many times before, and said nothing.

*

Noemi had forgotten how small liquor stores were here. The only person working the place was Mr. Danvers, a stocky man she remembered as a classmate's chatty father. Initially she was polite, listened to him carry on about the weather and his wife, but eventually she got tired of staring at candy and gum and started to lumber up and down the aisles, taking things on and off the shelves as he loudly rambled on from behind the counter about his brilliant son at UC Davis. The store's door jingled open and she hoped the extra customer would save her, but they hadn't. Mr. Danvers simply moved on from his college son to his lawyer daughter.

Noemi opened and closed the doors of the refrigerated section, catching glimpses of herself as the fluorescence bounced off the glass. Her dark curls hung limply over her shoulders, her olive skin was pale with the sunless days, and the bags under her eyes made her face look long and drawn. She frowned. She was nearing thirty, but she felt closer to seventy.

She impulsively grabbed a can of sweet tea, fingers creaking from the cold, and slowly made her way back to the counter to pick out her father's Camels. Mr. Danvers had been in the middle of saying something about his daughter's money when he noticed Noemi looking over his shoulder.

He followed her gaze to the cigarettes. "See something you like?"

"Camels. They're for my dad."

"Erwin's in town too? Gosh, I haven't seen him in years. How's he been? Does he still smoke them unfiltered?"

Noemi didn't get a chance to answer when Trish Parlor suddenly appeared next to her, emerging from the bowels of the liquor aisle like a red-haired harpy.

"Fancy seeing you here."

Noemi's eye twitched. "I'm allowed to be here, Trish."

For the first time since she got to the store, Mr. Danvers was completely silent.

Trish tilted her head. "Oh, I know that. I'm just surprised you stuck around."

"Why are you surprised?"

"Just thought you'd want to get out of here as soon as possible. What, with your dad and all."

Noemi's teeth set. "What does my dad have to do with this?"

"Nothing. It's just no one thought he would show his face around here ever again after the whole thing with your mom and Lucas, so the fact that he's *still* here with you is making a splash. It's all anyone's talking about. Did you know Erwin Reid was back in town, Mr. Danvers?"

Mr. Danvers looked cautiously between Trish and Noemi. "Noemi here just told me." He laid down three Camels and pointed to the sweet tea. "Is that gonna be all?"

Noemi nodded stiffly, rifling through her wallet as she heard Trish flutter her hands over candy wrappers.

"So he hasn't exactly *advertised* the fact that he's still here, has he?"

The cash register's clunky buttons sounded dull to the building thunder in Noemi's ears. "He's here to pay respects to my mother."

"Oh, I'm not doubting that, but even *you* have to admit that we all know Erwin Reid loves a good scandal."

The cherry-puckered smirk made Noemi sick.

"What's that supposed to mean?"

"Noemi, come on. You can't be playing this part, too. You can talk to me about him. I won't judge."

"Judge *what*, exactly?"

Trish realized she struck a nerve, and while her smile turned down, her eyes flamed bright. "Oh, you know what."

"I don't think I do."

"Who could forget who he abandoned you and your mom for?"

"And who could forget the girl who spread rumors about my mother fucking the mayor for a green card?"

Trish seemed taken aback. "Wow. I didn't think you'd still be mad about that."

"Well, I am."

"Please, Noemi. That was so long ago. It didn't mean anything."

"If you want to talk shit about my family, maybe you should call your chewed-up crew and jerk each other off for a bit. I'm sure they'd love to reminisce about how you all peaked in high school."

"Holy hell, Noemi. You're definitely different from what I remember."

Noemi turned her shoulders and chest towards Trish. "Yeah? And what is it you remember? Because what I remember was being bullied by a depressing wannabe-daddy's girl who had to make shit up about other people in order to feel better about her boring life."

"You know what? Fuck you, Reid."

"Fuck you too, Parlor. Happy to hear you're still a pathetic loser."

Noemi slammed down a ten-dollar bill and shoved the Camels in her jacket pocket. She went to grab the sweet tea when Trish said, "I'd rather be a loser than have a queer for a father."

Noemi dropped the can and cracked the flat of her palm against Trish's face, and before she could think about what she had done Trish had lunged and it became hands, hair, nails, fists, feet, guttural screams and blind blows, until Noemi curled up her hand and struck outwards, hitting bone and pulling back to see blood trickle over Trish's mouth, and Mr. Danvers had ran out from behind the counter to hold Noemi back, shouting in a blind panic for the sheriff's number, but Noemi shoved him away and stormed past Trish, reaching over to the candy bars and hurling a fistful of them at her before ramming through the store's door and surging into the howling winds.

*

"What the hell happened?"

She held out his smokes to him.

"Here you go."

"Is that blood on your hand?"

She glanced down at her knuckles, studying the faint streak of red there. "I don't think it's mine."

He pulled her into his room and shut the door behind her. "Noemi, what happened?"

"Nothing happened."

"Well something certainly happened, otherwise I wouldn't have gotten a call from the sheriff's office telling me you assaulted Patricia Parlor."

"I didn't *assault* her."

"I know you did because you just told me that the blood on your hand isn't yours."

"It's fine."

"It's *not* fine. She is the *sheriff's* daughter."

"So?"

"So? Did you even think of the kind of consequences that could have?"

"I don't live here anymore, so what does it matter to me?"

"Noemi, what's going on with you? You're walking around like you want to burn the world down. This isn't you."

"My *mother* just died. I don't know why you and everyone else seems to keep forgetting that."

"I haven't forgotten a damn thing. I know you're hurting, but that's no excuse to talk to me like that."

"I can talk to you however I want."

"Noemi Gabrielle."

"What are you gonna do? Ground me? I'm an adult."

"And I'm your father."

"You sure have a weird way of showing it."

"What did you just say?"

"Considering I wasn't even sure you were coming to my mother's funeral, I think it's funny that you suddenly want my respect when you don't want me to know anything about you at all."

"And just what is that supposed to mean?"

"It means that you haven't acted like a dad to me the entire time I've been growing up, so why should I even treat you like one?"

"You better take that back right now."

"Tell me I'm wrong."

"I've paid for the food on your plate and the roof over your head, don't you dare tell me I never provided for you."

"I'm talking about *having me around*, not providing for me. I'm talking about all the times you've shut me out and let me go like I don't fucking matter."

"What the hell are you even talking about?"

"You would return me to mom every single Sunday before noon even though I begged you to let me stay until dinner. You would never have me around for the holidays, even though I asked to be with you every year. You wouldn't even pick me up from school."

"That's just ridiculous, Noemi. I couldn't control that. It was part of the custody agreement."

"My mom would have let you keep me if you showed any indication you wanted me."

"I wanted you all the time, Noemi. I missed you like hell when you weren't around."

"Then why didn't you fight to keep me?"

"Because your mother would have taken you from me completely if I did!"

"That's not true and you know it! I know you and mom didn't end on good terms, but she wasn't cruel. She only wanted you to be happy, she told me that all the time, and if you gave any indication that you were the least bit happy with me then she would've fixed it."

"I was—I *am* happy with you. You're my daughter, of course you make me happy."

"I don't even know you!"

"If this is how you want to act around me then maybe that's for the best."

"Oh, that's rich, considering I learned everything from you."

"You talk to me like that one more time and I'm kicking you out of this room."

Noemi laughed bitterly. "Great. I don't know why I expected anything different."

"Alright, get out. You're in no mood to talk seriously with me, so we might as well—"

"I've always wanted to talk to you. Always. But you seem determined to make sure I want nothing less and I don't know what I did to deserve that."

He knew she was right, and she could see it in the way he looked away from her. "Noemi—"

"I know you see me and you just see a product from your other life, the one that made you miserable—"

"*I do not.* Don't ever—"

"—and I'm sorry I can't make that easier for you."

"—say that. *Noemi.*"

"It's fine. I get it. Enjoy your smokes."

When she walked out, he didn't come after her.

*

Noemi hadn't been able to sleep on her last night in South Creek.

She kept falling into shapeless terrors every time she closed her eyes, found herself staring into dark water and sinking to the bottom, unable to breathe, and by the time she gave up on trying to soothe herself into sleep the sun had already made its full ascension into the silvery morning. She showered, brushed her teeth, and had everything packed up by ten.

She was getting ready to head out when her father called. She stared at the screen for a moment before answering.

"Hi, dad."

"*Hi, Noemi.*"

His voice sounded shaky. She tried to be smooth, unbothered.

"How are you?"

"*I'm alright.*"

"Just alright?"

There was a silence, and then, "*You're still in South Creek?*"

"Yes. Are you?"

"*Yes.*" He cleared his throat. "*Do you want to meet me at the boardwalk in an hour?*"

"Sure. I've gotta leave before noon for my bus though."

"*Alright. See you soon.*"

"See you."

Noemi gathered up her bags over her shoulders and headed to South Creek Boardwalk. She studied the cracks in the pavement as she crossed streets and passed family-owned shops, kept her head down to avoid scornful eyes, and wondered why her mother never found it in herself to leave a town with so many fissures in its foundation. The streets began to slope downward towards the water, and the boardwalk came into view. It wasn't much of a boardwalk; it was more of a stunted pier with a clear view of distant hills that fanned around a gulf of water that flowed from the ocean. It was just as she remembered it.

She could see a lonely silhouette leaning on the railing, gilded by the sun, and she immediately recognized the broad shoulders and denim jacket.

She soundlessly drifted next to him and set down her bags, leaning her elbows on the rusty railing and crossing her ankles, mirroring his stance. They didn't look at each other.

"How'd you sleep?" she asked, trying to slide back into

something they were both familiar with, but when she turned to look at him, he had his hand over his eyes. She thought he might have a headache.

The water lapped beneath them, a gentle ebb as the ocean roiled in from the outside and died into a lurching rhythm. She peered down into the water, searching beneath the dark surface for something that could burst through the flat glides of calm waves, something that could shake this town apart and leave it raw and bare to the somber skies that hovered just above them. But that could take years, and Noemi only had until noon.

"Are you hungry?" she asked her dad, wondering if that's what he wanted. She looked at him again. His hand had come away from his eyes, but he was looking down into the water.

"Noemi. I want to apologize for yesterday."

"No, dad, it's okay, I was—"

"It's *not* okay. I didn't—It's not okay. It's not okay that you've been feeling that way and never told me."

"Dad." She considered lying. *I'm alright. I didn't mean it. I'm in a rough spot.* But then he looked at her, and for the first time she could see him beginning to show her what hid beneath the hard mask. She relented. "I wanted to say something sooner, but I didn't know how."

He sighed heavily. "I don't want you to be like me."

"I am like you, I'm your daughter."

"But you don't need to be *like* me. You don't need…" He stopped, searching for the words. "You don't need to hide behind another version of you, and I see you doing that now. Now that I think about it, I've seen you doing that for a while."

Noemi kicked the toe of her boot against the railing. "I don't know what you want to hear."

He didn't say anything.

Her mother had always said that Erwin Reid was the type of man who lived deep within himself, and that was all Noemi knew. She knew there was a life he had kept to himself, a life only he felt safe in, a life he shielded from prying eyes. She wondered if he could see the shield she was building as she tried to find her own life beyond him. She loved him dearly, loved him so much it felt like an open wound, but she had begun to question why it had to hurt so deeply once her mother died. Once the one person she felt she could truly be safe with was gone.

Mark already had a family and she could never let South Creek be a part of her. The scars on the road would swallow her up and drain her out into the sea until there was nothing left of her, and she dreaded the day that current would come for her. When she looked up at her dad, he let her see that same dread in him, just as she let him see it in her. And maybe he had gotten tired of trying to float in his own private world.

"I never wanted you to suffer because of me, Noemi. I know you have, and it kills me that I can never take any of that back."

Her chest tightened. "I never suffered because of you."

"Sometimes I feel like that's all I made you do."

"Dad, that's not true. I just wanted you to be happy, but it's this place, this town, it just makes us so..."

"We can only blame the town for so long, Emi."

Noemi remembered the home they had in South Creek. Tense family dinners, quiet Christmases, silences that slithered under the floorboards in search of minutes to swallow. She remembered the empty spaces her father constantly left behind, the shapes of him lost in the walls and the doorways.

"Can I ask you something?"

He hesitated. "Go ahead."

"Was it something I did?" He looked confused, so she went on. "Was it something I said that made you feel like you couldn't talk to me?"

He shut his eyes, shook his head. "It's nothing you ever did, Noemi."

"Then why—"

"Listen to me. I did a lot of things I regret. I've done a lot of things that hurt people. That hurt Lucas. That hurt your mom, rest her soul. I've regretted the pain I've put you through, but the one thing I never regretted—and never will regret—is you."

The only time he talked like this, uninterrupted by his own painful self-awareness, was when he was in the apartment he had with Uncle Lucas. That small but joyful space, with its sunlit kitchen and bedrooms that smelled of woodsy colognes and cigarette smoke. That corner of the world filled with their shared laughter and secret smiles.

Noemi couldn't say anything, so he took her silence and held it gently in his voice for the first time in a long time.

"I want you to stay with me and your Uncle Lucas for a while. For a few weeks. Or months. However long you can. If that's what you want too."

She didn't know if that's what she needed, she didn't know if her Uncle Lucas knew she'd be coming, she didn't know what she would do with so much time there. She had never stayed for more than a weekend; she had never been welcomed to linger in that world.

But then she said, "Alright," without thinking about it for too long, and she remembered their warm carpet, their cigarette smoke, their orange peel walls, and she thought of home for a while.

He placed a warm hand over hers. "Then let's go."

He picked up her bags, waving her away when she offered to help, and she smiled as they left behind the salty breezes of South Creek's boardwalk.

SAPLING

L. Kardon

it's useless to try to explain my sexuality because, honestly, it's
not one particular way. but i do know that i had flipped the off
switch for a number of years and packed desire away with my
skinny jeans because maybe that's just what happens when your
body is blown open from the inside and you adopt the worried-
crow slouch beneath the burden of parenting. and in that home,
at that time, there wasn't much to get aroused about anyway.
and it was around then when i really started to feel it, how little
i enjoyed the feeling of being stuffed full of organs and kind
of banged against and strangled a little, and there'd been a lot
of that in the last two decades or so, not the consensual kind,
the reluctant, exhausting kind. whatever erotic fire i had left was
no more than an almost-extinguished ember that i occasionally
blew on in the dark night of the night, alone in the bathroom
after the baby was asleep and imagining some pixie-haired
domme serving me little lashes. i thought my mating instinct
was in the trashcan with my placenta and the ring my child's
father had given me, or somesuch, but i'll tell you what, a year
or two after leaving, warm feelings did return, and whenever
a cute dyke walked in the room or a flanneled queer ordered
a beer well, yes, i felt young again (but also shy and insecure
but perhaps that's young). i recalled the summer when my best
friend fucked me with a zucchini til the harvest moon grew fat.
i thought about that other beauty who's too ethereal and magic-
made to ever notice that she makes my palms sweat and to this
day when she calls me i blush thinking about her hipbones. i felt
wide eyed watching disheveled, overworked moms cast razor

sharp looks at obstructions and i wanted to brush their hair
and kiss the tops of their ears. i made up dreamy queers who i
gazed at in my cider and felt very bashful when my eyes locked
with an actual human, and i didn't feel queer enough, and that's
awkward because i wasn't straight either. but it's all to say; don't
give up, you have a longing in you still.

ETHNIC ORIGIN (CIRCLE ONE)

M.A. Dubbs

My stomach folds over
as I'm back at el supermercado and failing
to hide my glacial whiteness behind
overstretched sleeves.
I want to coat myself with cumin
for a sun-licked bronze look
and wash out my goldenrod hue with some mole
for locks of coal horse hairs.
The kind señoritas in flamenco skirts
with terracotta lips have.
The kind that I should have…

At the register we trade broken languages
porque gringas no hablan español and
the tamale lady that comes on Sundays
sneers at me through a rainbow of
plastic rosary beads (*es una pena,
los maricones lo arruinaron, ella reflexiona*).

Prayer cards, tall glass candles of Our Lady
(*¿Es ella mi dama si soy una mariposa?*)
strung out where the candy should be.
The cashier lobs my pink concha in a bag,
my bisabuela's heart in a white
lunch sack, and smashes Abuelita's-
Nestlé's -boxed chocolate on top.

Spanish collapses
and tildes become serpents
slinking inside the aisles, rolling
their "r"s with a proper
deep throat vibration.
Miniature mariachis
ride on their backs
hunting for some güera.
Their "Ay ya ya"s,
from lane cinco,
breaks this jaguar
warrior's heart and I
melt into snow.

The Strange Birth of Pad Thai

Polchate (Jam) Kraprayoon

My grandma claimed the best place for pad Thai
was by a movie-house,
down in the Chinese quarter of town.
She'd sit and watch the cooks toss in
tofu, radish, shrimp, and shallots
as people in the cinema shuffled out.

Shunt that jumble to the wok's far side,
fry up an egg, blend it in
a thickened mix of noodles, sprouts,
palm sugar and tamarind.
Once done, each little dish was wrapped
in dried leaves and wax paper.

Now, that no-name shop is gone
its falling chili flakes
and peanut dust swept up and swallowed
by the cold clock of 'Progress,'
or was it merely change?

Frankly, I don't like pad Thai,
each spoonful slicked with oil
too sweet, cloying, on the tongue
but Thais never say, 'I don't *like* to eat this.'
Rather we say, *kin mai pen*, meaning:
'I don't know *how* to eat it.'

This wording suggests
I could learn to love pad Thai,
love it like my grandmother learned to
after the government ordered everyone
to 'Buy Thai,' 'Be Thai,' and 'Eat Thai.'

Our dear leader ordered the country
to wear western hats, to scrub
their betel-black teeth white,
and stuff their stomachs up
with steaming plates of pad Thai.

This dish, our nimble diplomat,
convinced would-be colonists
that we were a proper country,
not one of those ramshackle places
you send gunboats to and take over.

My grandma closely watched
those noodles sizzle and slither
in that hot wok before
she pulled back the grease-soaked leaves
to find underneath the Chinese chives,
things like King, Faith, and Nation.

AUNTIE PAT'S FRIED CHICKEN

LeShun Smith

Ever since I was a little boy, I associated some of my loved ones with what I felt was their best attribute, or just something they did really well. As a single mother, my mother conquered several challenges well, so in my eyes, she's a superwoman. My uncle was physically strong, he could snatch a spark plug out of an engine block with his bare hands, so I labeled him the hulk. My Auntie Pat is an amazing cook. I always felt that was her way of expressing love because everything tasted so good, like she put her heart in it. Within her repertoire of deliciousness is the best fried chicken in the world. The kind where you eat one piece and start questioning your allegiances to other foods.

Not only that, I also felt guilty and disloyal to my other aunts over Auntie Pat's chicken and other dishes. I ignorantly assumed I was supposed to be closer to my other aunts because we were biologically related. It seemed an abomination for me to sever ties over chicken, but I did it time and time again. Pat became my favorite auntie. I'm still not sure if she's my favorite because of her talent with frying chicken or because of the kind of person she is.

If the word nice had a face, you'd see my Auntie Pat. She had kind, inviting eyes, with a warm smile that was so infectious you couldn't help but start grinning yourself. She was also hip, surprisingly youthful, and she sat alone on the throne as the undisputed Queen of Fried Chicken!

Since, as a whole, we were a close-knit family, with roots

in the deep south, family gatherings were normal. At least one or two weekends out of each month, the grown-ups would either get together and go bar hopping or they all picked a family member's house to lounge in and have an impromptu game night. That usually consisted of playing spades or poker and drinking alcohol in excess. All of the kids, ages ranging from 6 to 15 years old, would have to pick whose house they wanted to go to. Depending on the choices and the availability of any grown up, the older kids usually had to take care of the young kids. Normally that would be ok, but it lacks an essential ingredient, chicken!

I was young, maybe 6 or 7, but I knew how to influence people to see things my way. So, I and some cousins my age used to strategize on whose house we wanted to go to. Our decisions were based on who had recently gone grocery shopping and who would let us play and stay up late. Auntie Pat was always everyone's choice, but I was her #1 salesman. I knew my Auntie Pat to be even-tempered, patient, off on the weekends; she didn't go out to every family function, she rented movies on Fridays after work, she also had cable, loved music and cooking, and most of all, she'd rather her 3 kids (my cousins & partners) sleep in their own beds. When we made that pitch as a unit, it always made it hard for her to deny us. However, I later learned I would have more success on my own.

Even now, as a grown man, just the thought of her fills my nostrils with the smell of garlic and Lawry's seasoning salt; I can hear the crackling sounds of that frying joyfulness I love so much. One night at my Auntie Pat's house, my cousins and I were playing hide and seek. Usually the kitchen was off limits because my Auntie Pat would be cooking. But this night was different, I wanted to know how Auntie Pat got the chicken to taste so good. The crust had the crunchy consistency of a sour cream & onion Pringle chip. The meat was tender and savory. I knew I had to find a way into that kitchen. Each time

I was hiding, I hid somewhere around the kitchen. One time I hid in the hallway closet in front of the kitchen, so I could see her process. Another time, I hid in that small slot adjacent to the kitchen that housed the ironing board. But then I caught a glimpse of that infectious and warm smile of my auntie as she vibed out to her ol' school music. You know, that 1970's Rhythm & Blues that's nostalgic and synonymous with family, culture, and simpler times in nearly every Black household. Specifically, it was Al Green's "Let's Stay Together;" she was lip synching in perfect synchronicity as she danced and cooked. My auntie had this magnetic quality about her that drew people in, grown-ups and kids alike. It's like all those people who followed Jesus for days just to touch the hem of His garment, be healed, or acknowledged by him. Auntie Pat made me feel important and seen.

Seeing Auntie Pat dance her two-step and sway her hips from side to side, I couldn't help but feel tempted to go and dance with her. When I entered the kitchen, trying to jam with my auntie, even she knew that the dancing was merely a conduit to seeing her process. So, without missing a step, she directed me to wash my hands. Then she handed me the batter bag with flour and spices spanning the myriad of peppers, garlic, and herbs I never knew the names of. I thought to myself, the secret must be in the batter, and she trusted me with it.

Boy was I wrong! As I was shimmying and shaking the bag, she allowed me to drop a few drumsticks in. My mind didn't quite capture what she was doing with a brush with long soft bristles and a bowl of sauce, with two other platters of drumsticks. When she felt I was shaking myself silly, she tapped me on the shoulder, motioning for me to put the chicken in the frying pan. Breaking my rhythm, I felt the moment of truth had arrived. I thought what I was doing was the most important part of her process. We continued in that fashion until all the chicken was cooked and strained. Then finally, I was the first to taste what we had done. Auntie Pat's Fried Chicken tastes like the marriage between Popeye's crunchy chicken and Kentucky Fried Chicken's original recipe, and they swung with a five-star restaurant. Ghetto-licious!

As if my Auntie Pat wasn't awesome enough, one time we went to Six Flags / Great America in Gurnee, IL. To prepare for the trip and ride, Auntie Pat fried a bunch of wings and made some little square spiced ham/luncheon meat sandwiches, with cheese and Miracle Whip. I think this was around the time when Coke II was the number one soda. Maybe it was 1990. Yeah it was that year, because that's when Six Flags unveiled the Batman ride, and it was the very reason we were taking this trip. Once inside the park, I was consumed with excitement. The plan was to do the park in sections, starting from the front. We hit the Shockwave, Viper, Merry-go-round, and some other mild rides. We even stopped and played games at the huts, like the shooting gallery, the ball & bottle game, and balloon darts. Before we knew it, it was lunch time. I was like, YES! I was eager to get to the car to get to the chicken, but mine was a minority view. My other cousins wanted burgers and chili cheese fries. Don't get me wrong, I like that stuff too. But when compared to Auntie Pat's fried chicken, all bets are off! So, my auntie decided that a few of us would go to the car to eat while everyone else ate in the park. When done, we were to meet up at Splash Waterfalls in the center of the park. I went to that car and got chicken wasted! To this day, when I see, smell, or eat chicken I think of Auntie Pat.

I haven't seen my Auntie Pat in twenty-one years. I recently heard she doesn't even eat or cook fried chicken anymore. That's when I truly realized it was never really about chicken or food, for that matter, there was a more important lesson learned and involved. Food was only a pawn in the battle to maintain our love, unity, and family structure. If it takes a village to raise a child, then how do you bring that village together? FOOD!

CHICKEN! Through frequent family gatherings, my family was teaching us to value one another and nurture one another. Without making the connection until now, I realized these are the lessons I've been preaching to my son. So, I was Mr. Miagied or Daniel Sonned! My Auntie Pat not only catered to my love for her chicken, she was instrumental in shaping who I am. Coming to this realization, my love for my Auntie Pat has increased tenfold. As soon as I'm released, with her blessing, I'll use her recipe to fry chicken and reunite our family with those old lessons in love, unity, and family structure.

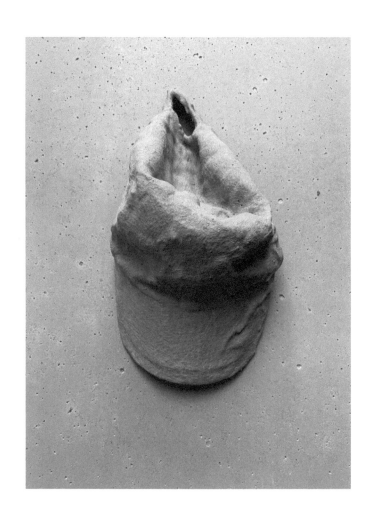

Was My Father

CONCRETE SCULPTURE

Mario Loprete

SAND MIRROR

PHOTOGRAPHY

Guilherme Bergamini

THE MIRRORS OVER THE BASIN ARE LINED WITH ROWS OF MEDICINE-

VANITAS

PHOTOMONTAGE

Carrie Albert

INFLUENCER

ACRYLIC ON PAPER

Ali Headley

UNTITLED

ANALOGUE COLLAGE

Coco Spencer

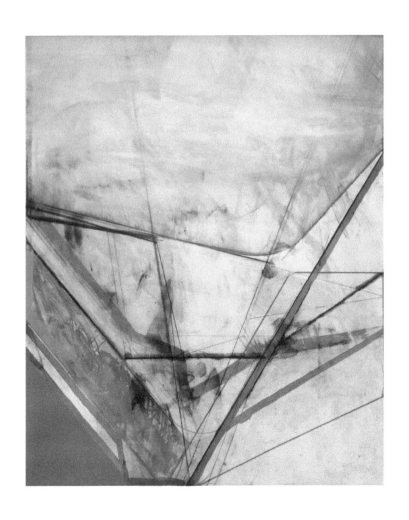

DOUBLE FALLS

ACRYLIC & COLORED PENCIL ON PAPER

Nick Lamia

ANNOTATING AN INSTAGRAM 2

MAGAZINE COLLAGE ON PAPER

Katlin Marisol Sweeney

SLEEPING PERSONA

MIXED MEDIA

Keily V. Maldonado

IDENTITY & MINDSET

DIGITAL ILLUSTRATION

Gregory Francis Royse II

MIRROR
OIL & COLLAGE ON BOARD

Kateryna Bortsova

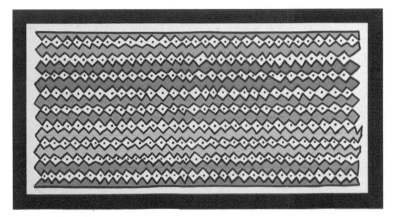

SERENITY
ACRYLIC ON CANVAS

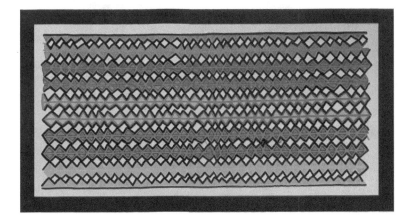

MANIA
ACRYLIC ON CANVAS

Matty Penner

Stairs Maze. 2021

STAIRS MAZE

COLLAGE ON ACID-FREE PAPER

Ernst Perdriel

Hope Is an EBT Card

Shannon Steinkamp

tucked into the middle pocket
of my mother's purse

WINDHAM

Robert Bear

Windham Township, nestled uncomfortably deep within the Appalachian Mountains, claims a population of eight hundred and ten poor white souls. It comes with a layer of ash on anything that sits for more than a few hours, and it features the pungent aroma of sauerkraut, both of which come from the paper mill across the Susquehanna River.

No one has ever looked up the history of Windham, and no one has ever been curious about the ten best things to do when visiting the place. The town is on no one's list of the nicest, safest, or prettiest places to visit in America, and the only list it does frequent is that of towns you can most readily find meth being manufactured.

Next to the paper mill, meth manufacture is the largest employer of the county.

Unlicensed massage parlors that offer a happy ending run a close third.

Windham's main street runs parallel to the town's single creek, a tributary to the Susquehanna River. It's a winding strip of grey asphalt through dirtied snow, heaped in large chunks by the township's snowplow.

Homes are lined up on either side, each one aged and in some state of disrepair. In their front yards, deer carcasses hang by their rear legs, from the branches of trees normally reserved for a tire swing that would hang during mild summer days.

Most of the houses have one too many cars and a few too many rusting children's toys in their driveway.

There are no children in Windham; I'm not sure if there ever have been.

The further I drive toward my childhood home, the more nauseated I become. It had been thirty years since I had seen the place, and if circumstances hadn't dictated my return, it would have happily been another thirty.

As it happens, my return coincides with my father's death. So, it isn't all bad.

LEYLINE

Tomas Nieto

In the morning, I left my little room on Broad
with only two suitcases—
everything else went back into the great ecology
of used furniture lining the streets of San Francisco.
All of me was stripped from this room
and the only things left
were the scratches and stains.
One from the day I moved in,
another from my bookshelf, some from
misfortune and a few from history.
My whole deposit gone.
My chair leg imprinted
into the door frame, dried Hoisin sauce
in the hardwood. An outline
of my makeshift closet lived
in the corner, and good nights
were etched beneath the window.
On the largest wall,
the tape from my thesis notes
left a series of tears in the eggshell.
They looked like Morse code, or a melody
on a lineless staff, or a flock
of swallows migrating south.

The symmetry of a hello and goodbye:
the sacred geometry of a cut.

American Me

Andres Enrique Mendoza

American me,
Watches the news:
as a child prosecutes
the Mesican.

HATE the Mesican!
JAIL the Mesican!

..Wait I am a Mesican..

Speaking Spanish to my English teachers..
Next day I'm in E-L-D.

Going back to the barrios and everything I see is
Mescan,
if a song emanated from my mouth
it was in Spanish.
So why do we hate Mescan?

"Ask them honey."
"Hi! WHERE IS YOUR MOM-O? DO YOU, oh I don't know
about this honey, DO YOU SPEAK-O ENGLISH?"

Why do you ask me?
I am American?
Wait no...Yes...
Right?

Make me walk like you
Even talk like you,
But my Mescan skin tan and kin
Say otherwise..
Southernize my accent!
Bully my *Caló*
and now we're "Civilized Folk."
But Cesar Chavez
and the brown berets,
held the front
down,
and fought
along.
Corky's words ring inside my head
..Stupid America...
Wait John weren't you Meskin?
How many generations have been victims?
Of the border crossing us?
Something is missing here.
Somewhere in the history books?
History crooks!
I was in the Civil War but never mentioned?
I was in World War I and was never mentioned?
I was in World War II and was never mentioned?!
Guy Gabaldon was Mescan?!
In Vietnam, my blood spilled across the jungles and
my body endlessly tumbled down hills.
While General Lee kicked and fumbled around
In makeshift towns full of Mexi-cans?
Oh wait!
I forgot the Korean wars,
Ri-i-i-i-ght,

because they didn't want to hear us dying.
I'm fearing my own loss within
the school books
        and prison blocks
Full of Mexicans.
Detest me
Invest my fragile soul
In jail
To own my piece of mind,
Wait no,
      to find my own peace of mind.

MANYWHERE
Dale Stromberg

If the crescent moon at the start of the month is an opening parenthesis,
and the crescent moon at the end of the month is a closing parenthesis,
then all the month but the night of the new moon is merely an aside.

Bellatrix Sakakino received a mysterious package in the post: a thumb drive folded within a sheet of A4 paper which read, in black Sharpie, "I thought you should know."

The data on the drive left her thunderstruck. She learned that, immediately after she was born, the obstetrician had harvested blood rich in stem cells from her umbilical cord, and researchers had used a revolutionary laboratory technique to make an exact clone of her, with one difference. By altering the DMRT1 gene on the ninth chromosome, they had made the clone male. Chromosome for chromosome, she and her unknown twin were otherwise genetically identical. Only their sexes were reversed.

According to the thumb drive, his name was Nao Hovgaard. He worked in a hair salon in Hamadayama, just up the Inokashira Line. She made an appointment for a trim.

Not fifteen minutes after she settled into the swivel chair and he draped a vinyl cover over her, with surreal ease they fell in love. There was no other word for it but fate. To keep things simple, she pretended it had been a chance meeting. They saw each other daily after that.

He was ten months her junior, but neither cared. The tendency to muse during lulls in conversation—the dislike of crowds or loud public spaces—the almost pathological antipathy toward doing uninteresting tasks... Their similarities were striking. One morning, Nao commented on this. "It's like I was designed to be with you. Like I have a gene to love you."

"It's not like our lives are determined by our genes, though," Bellatrix murmured, uneasy.

"You're wrong." His hair had fallen over his face, covering one eye. "People only think they're free." He looked so alluring, half obscured.

"But that's..." Lost again in him, she never completed the thought.

She should have thrown out the thumb drive, or at least hidden it better. He'd been watching YouTube when she drifted to sleep one Sunday after lunch; when she awoke, his face was drained white.

"How much did you read?"

"Everything."

"I was going to tell you," she lied.

He stared, rigid. "Our kids would be... inbred." Nao had always wanted children.

Bellatrix began silently to cry. "Self-bred." *They would be us*, she wanted to add, to protest. *Wholly one hundred percent us. Parents love children who are half them, so we would love our children twice as much.* But words failed her.

"God, how... creepy." He shut the door gently when he left.

As I love you wholly, she called silently after. It was no use. She could never have won him back because she could never have reconciled two things she knew at her very core: That he was right, and that he was wrong. She was wiser than he, and she was a fool.

In the years since, Bellatrix has often reflected that all her life up to the day they met had been a prelude, and that her every day since has been an echo of a lingering note. She walks as one dead, hollowed out by loneliness. She has never forgiven him for thwarting her fate.

comPATRIOTS

RC deWinter

the country
is quaking // shaking //
opening
veins where red
meets blue // then
drowning us in an ocean
of violet and

violence //
skin on skin in the
streets // words that
drip blood in
print // in pixels flying through
the ether // to land

sharp on skin
already bruised by
too many
wrongs // how can
we heal when everything is
designed to keep us raw //

quivering //
suspicious of our
own shadows //

can we come
together in our common
humanity or

will we fall //
fodder in the war
on freedom //
i am you //
you are me // we are not each
other's enemy //

JANE'S VEINS

Allison Whittenberg

Two diaries: one lies, the other dreams until reality
Loops into illusion.
Neither records terrorist attacks, murder rates, or evolving
leaders.
One contains measurements of her bust size; one holds
friendship and love, pursued, sustained, or in need of
resuscitation.
Both contain hate for prettier girls.
Each smells soft as if sprinkled with powder.
One is black and plain, that's kept under her bed.
The other is pink and has birds and flowers on the cover that's
often on her desk.
The world is microscopic. Each night as her wrist moves the
pages, she scripts with red juice.

SUPER BOWL COMMERCIAL WRITTEN BY AI

Jeffrey H. MacLachlan

I have duplicated a key to unlock your high school self. A
key is something you can purchase for a popular party you
never attended. Brainwaves need to be gentrified by marketing
rhetoric because human culture is lemon sour, but their labor
is divine. Guzzle soda through a slender straw while zipping
around in luxury. Look at this attractive couple. Look at
how they nod at a minimalist loveseat. Their faces are the
temperature of an upturned stone. Mimic their smiles. Mimic
their smiles. Mimic their smiles.

Thank you, I needed that. Here are three celebrities. I
understand their context is the opposite context you'd
expect and so therefore this is an amusing experience. To be
unentertained is to be drained is to be bored is to be hollow.
Let's go on a magical dream date. You may touch me in areas
not designed for reproduction because this is for nuclear
family consumption. Hold the beverage with one hand and
express yourself with the other. This is to display openness in a
defensive stance. Defense wins romantic championships, which
is the goal of these thirty seconds.

QUARANTINE SELF-PORTRAIT
Madi Giovina

unbrushed teeth / untrimmed nails / the restlessness / the
helplessness / things becoming more & less important /
morning walks around the living room / evening walks around
the kitchen / consuming, consuming / a birthday party on
zoom / a graduation party on zoom / a funeral wake on zoom
/ uninstalling zoom / a cancelled wedding / a cancelled book
fair / a cancelled Very Powerful Man / lots of these, Cancelled
Men / someone saying "the new normal" / someone else
saying "scamdemic" / staring at screens / breathing in smoke
/ breathing out lorazepam / symptom checking / so much
symptom checking / getting paid, some weeks / hearing the
neighbors fighting / trying not to listen / all of my friends
getting kittens / drinking more / drinking less / putting
food in jars for later / hoping there will be a later / all of the
jarred food expiring / losing track of time / finding it again /
consuming, consuming

ENTOMOLOGY

Aimee Lowenstern

Here is how the metaphor works—
Here is how I work—
Here is how my brain stutters
on the periphery of consciousness,
tapping dragonfly wings against the window
of your mind's eye;

Here is the tooth and tongue of it: I
am disabled in my body,
and by the fact that I have a body—

Glass-jar trapped,
nostrils and mouth, I
make holes for air.

What am I? A thought—
I'm not sure which one.
A hive mind/my mind hive,
these ants like beads of blood
tunneling veins,
running on instinct,
running all up and down
the sides of the glass.

THE IMAGE OF SAND

McKenna Themm

Footprints are a language I read
when I am
walking slow
along the coast. The green palms
shading my face
like an umbrella
wave farewell
to tired eyes and
lonely hands,
to second tries
and one second's
glance at a face
I'll never see again.

I sometimes
study the footprints
of strangers
and try to understand
their messages—stepping
forward and placing
each of my toes, one
by one
in the respective grooves
of those who have
already left behind
their painted strokes
on the canvas of the beach.

I try to hear the laughter
coming from the
small and wild prints
where the young girl runs squealing
into the water
covered in the remnants of
her fallen sandcastle.

I imagine the conversation
of the elderly couple
whose prints
side by side
vary in length
as they stop to take in
the glow of their final
evening together.

And I wonder if
a ghost or
another passerby
will understand how deeply
mine own marks upon
the sand
are imprinted with
grief
before the tide
rises again
and pulls them
into the sea.

IDENTITY

Emily Joy Oomen

My identity is a tapestry
Strung together by an unknown sewer
With mismatched cloths
Handed down to me from past generations

These cloths are all woven together
With an heirloom of thread
And colorful ribbons of personality

The tapestry is decorated
With bows of interests
And dyed in the colors of the environment

Although the tapestry is merely
A curious combination of antiquated old parts
Somehow it births a beauty
As much a wonder
As it is
The soul

My identity is a carpet tile
Pieced together by society
With generic cloths
From popular limited selection

These cloths are strung together
With an empty thread
And scratchy yarn

The small carpet is decorated
With empty words and numbers
And dyed in the colors of labels

Although the carpet is merely
An uncreative masterpiece of plastic parts
Somehow it births a dullness
As much empty
As it is
Nothing

MÍRAME

Eric Odynocki

"Gael Antonio Lara Martínez?" Coach Z stammered while taking attendance.

I looked up, surprised to hear such a name that sounded like one of my cousins' in Baja. Not that anyone in my Long Island high school would expect someone named Brett Applebaum to be Mexican. Besides my black hair, I did not fit anyone's stereotype of mom's side of the family. My light skin and hazel eyes all came from dad, features which allowed me to blend in with the rest of the student body, allowed me to overhear unsuspecting classmates who were comfortable enough in their homogeneity to joke about the Latin American day labourers that were beginning to gather on street corners.

Gael looked at us warily with large, dark brown eyes. He was short for a junior, skinny, like me. I saw something familiar in his gelled black hair, his nose and full lips; glimpses of relatives in mom's photo albums and the black and white portraits hanging in our hallway. He stood separate from us and I knew that feeling, looking at a group from a distance alone because of difference. But unlike Gael, I could hide mine. Because I had learned I should. Because in first grade when I shared that my mom was Mexican, Ms. Green told me to stop lying and the other kids stared at me. And when we studied Mesoamerica in fifth grade I got excited and I wanted to talk about how Tenochtitlan was built in the middle of a lake. Mr. Wright made me lower my hand when he stressed how the Aztecs sacrificed hundreds if not thousands of humans at a time by ripping out their victims' hearts. My classmates cringed and giggled at the horrific details.

Gael wore a jersey of the national Mexican soccer team and jeans which Coach Z pointed out was the wrong outfit for gym class. Gael only smiled sheepishly. Coach Z mumbled something under his breath and addressed the rest of us in our squads. And I wanted so badly to say something, to help, to be the bridge of communication. But having grown up speaking only English at home left mere clothing vocabulary lists from Spanish class to race through my head. Without realizing, an audible grunt escaped my mouth. I pretended to clear my throat when everyone looked in my direction. After an interminable pause, Coach Z told us to head out to the track to run the mile. On our mass exodus, Mike MacNamara imitated me to peals of laughter from his friends. For the rest of the class period I tried avoiding eye contact with Gael who, to everyone's unspoken surprise, outran even Mike.

*

I must have been four. Abuela's front door was painted the same deep green as the jade figurines in her hutch. The door reminded me of a Jolly Rancher. The floors were marble tile, the walls a stark white, and the aroma of corn tortillas hung in the air. The back patio was an enclosed oasis from the urban sprawl of Tijuana. There were tiers of philodendron, birds of paradise, and the twisting beauties of orchids in pearly whites, mottled magentas, and crimson. I weaved my way among the large clay pots, crouching beneath the gigantic leaves, unnoticed by the hummingbirds flitting about the flowers.

I spent a lot of time with my dad while mom chatted away with abuela and my aunts and uncles. My cousins darted through abuela's house from the front patio to the back playing one game or another, mostly soccer. The youngest of them was at least three years older than me. At first the age difference, language barrier, and my shyness prevented me from joining the tussle. But then one day, while the adults sat around the dining room table and talked, my cousins began playing a game on the front patio that looked too fun to resist. Each had a hat or towel or even a piece of paper hanging from their back. Someone played music from the radio and my cousins began chasing after one another, trying to snatch each other's hat or towel or piece of paper. Anyone who lost their item when the music stopped lost that round. I ran in circles with my cousins, laughed without breath, and a glow tickled my belly as I held up my trophies at the end of a round and Jorgito or Cristi or Chuyito patted me on the back or cheered my name.

Abuela's face is not so clear but I remember the warmth of her body when she hugged me, how her pink floral smock enveloped me. She would sit me on her lap and I would prattle on in English about my favorite toys and TV shows while crumbs of concha or other pan dulce speckled my lips and chin. If mom wasn't there to translate, abuela would nod and giggle anyway. But mostly I remember how her eyes creased in half moons of adoration when, after a few days of listening, I told her, "Te quiero."

*

A few weeks later we were outside on the field to play American football. Coach Z had begrudgingly reviewed the rules of the game, prefaced his instructions with an eye roll and, "For those of you who live under a rock." I smothered the urge to tell the Coach that anomalies to his perception of the world existed, that I was one such under-rock-dweller. It was moments like these that I regretted taking a different science class than my band friends. Our lab and gym periods alternated on different days leaving me no ally with whom to commiserate.

Coach Z chose Mike and another athlete to be captains. One by one, our classmates were selected until Gael and I were left. Mike's blue eyes switched between us, calculating losses. At last, he spat my name before turning around to huddle with the other students. Gael jogged over to the other team.

I did not need Mike to tell me to interfere as little as possible so I stood somewhere on the field where I expected the least amount of action while the others lined up in formation. As his team got into place, Gael stood in the neutral zone, his large eyes darting around. Coach Z took Gael by the shoulders and put him at the end of his team's line. The Coach pointed emphatically at the ground, said, "Aquí." I stifled a cringe as Gael smiled with embarrassment and Coach Z walked away satisfied with himself. Mike and his friends chuckled amongst themselves.

Coach Z blew the whistle. Bodies crashed into one another and the ball flew into the air. I jogged following its course but lost sight of it amid the tangle of legs and arms. The ball flew again and Gael caught it. He began to run towards my team's goal post. He crossed a few yards when Mike lunged at him and they both tumbled to the ground. Mike bounced back up, twirled the ball in the air. Gael, wincing, sat up. Mike turned back to him, reached out his hand. As Gael extended his palm, a smile lighting his face, Mike shoved him back to the ground. Gael rubbed the back of his head while he watched Mike jog over to his guffawing admirers.

I should have crossed that field, offered my hands as the rungs for Gael to pull himself up. But I stood frozen in place, as if imprisoned by the bone-white bars of the yard lines. Gael's dark eyes pinned my gawk, the questions in them like hooks at my throat. I reddened and my eyes darted over to Coach Z. His baseball cap faced down, hiding his gaze that at the moment was captivated with his clipboard.

*

I was eleven the last time we visited Mexico. The week was uneventful, or rather, less magical as on previous visits when abuela was still alive. She had been gone for two years by then. Mom cried when we passed by abuela's house. It had new owners. I cried too. I missed the patio. I missed abuela's baking. I missed the conversations I would never have with her.

We embarked on the obligatory pilgrimage to La Bufadora where we took family photos, the spray of the spout as our backdrop. We made the usual calls, stopping by various aunts and uncles for an asado and nieve. I hung out with my cousins who could speak English by then, talked about how boy bands were lame but Blink182 was sick—a descriptor that fascinated my cousins and resulted in us writing an impromptu glossary of American slang and their Mexican equivalents. Buena onda or padre was cool. Guácala meant gross. A fresa was a rich snob.

To cross the border back into the U.S. took three hours. In our rented minivan we blasted the AC to ward off the blazing Baja sun. Mom reminded me to be alert when the border patrol interviewed us, to be polite. "I know, I know," I said from the back seat. "Listen to your mother," dad said. I watched the vendors make their way up and down the lanes, offering elote, bottled water, and cups of mango drizzled with chamoy.

When we pulled up to the booth, I watched in silence as my mom gripped my dad's hand. The tendons in her forearm bulged. The agent—tall, bald, and blue-eyed—called out our names one by one as he flipped through our documents. He paused at mom's green passport. The agent fired off a round of questions in his hoarse voice. "Is this man your husband?" "What's his name?" "What's your business in the U.S.?" My mom answered with a quiver in her voice I didn't remember hearing before.

*

Each successive gym class was torture. It was both a relief and disappointment when Coach Z blew his whistle to end class; I was finally free of my own purgatorial awkwardness but another chance at friendship disappeared.

At least outside of gym I didn't have to think of Gael. Our schedules were so different that I never saw him in other parts of the school.

One day, though, I went with Patrick and Dwayne—friends from band—to sit in the commons during a free period. While we talked about how the cheerleader pyramid collapsed at the last basketball game we played at, something caught my eye. Without thinking I looked and saw Gael walking along the length of the commons. Before I could turn away we made eye contact. Something flashed in his face. Was it recognition? I panicked when I saw him nod with a slight smile. His pace slowed as if he would walk over. In answer I gave only the slightest of nods and quickly turned back to Patrick and Dwayne, laughing unnaturally loud at something they just said.

"Who's that?" Patrick asked.

I shook my head. "Just some kid from gym."

*

At dinner one night I successfully hid my preoccupation from my parents. I laughed with them over our meal of salad, chicken cutlets, and mashed potatoes. My eyes drifted over to the hutch that displayed the colorful dinnerware from Mexico my mom inherited from abuela, the sixteen-piece set that we never used, not even for special occasions.

When we finished eating, my dad went into the living room to watch the game. As usual, I stayed to wash dishes. We had a dishwasher but this was one of my parents' ways of keeping me "level headed." Mom stood next to me and wiped the plain white plates dry.

Sometimes while mom and I washed the dishes she would recount stories from her life and family lore. Like how she met my dad in a disco in San Diego. She was celebrating the end of the semester at UABC with her friends while he was out with a few other interns from the firm. Or she would talk about her childhood in Tijuana, the weekly outings to the movie theater down the block or the neighbors' scandals that sounded plucked from a telenovela. From her storytelling I learned about a great aunt who was a *soldadera* in the Mexican Revolution, how my great-grandfather dived for pearls. I cherished these stories, memorized them as best I could, as if by absorbing them I could understand what it is to be Mexican, become just as Mexican as I was American and Jewish. That night, my mom talked about how much she hated learning English in school: the weird sounds, the endless grammar exceptions that seemed to outnumber the rules. "And look where I ended up?" she concluded with a chuckle.

After a pause, I asked, "Mom, why didn't you ever teach me Spanish?"

My mom lifted her chin at the randomness of my question. "I don't know," she said. When her eyes met my entreating gaze she shrugged and with a small smile as if caught in a little white lie, she continued, "It just never happened. Your father only spoke English. Nobody else spoke Spanish in the neighborhood. It was the 80s. I was probably the only Mexican on Long Island back then."

I wanted to tell her about Gael, how much I wanted to talk to him. But I kept thinking about how I failed to stand up for him. "Sometimes I wish you had taught us Spanish," I said, handing her a plate.

"But you're learning it so well in school! You'll be fluent in no time." Her eyes narrowed at the plate. "Brett, be careful, this one still has a stain," she said, putting the plate back in the sink. "I want it spotless like all the others."

*

A few more weeks passed and Gael's smile never reappeared. Mike and his friends continued to exclude him, to make jokes at his expense, relishing the knowledge that ridicule is easy to understand regardless of language. Gael only glared. His fists balled once or twice but he never threw a punch. Perhaps he knew doing so would just get him in trouble. How would he explain himself in the principal's office? Who would the administration believe besides a star athlete? And I witnessed it all while I played the bare minimum, unnoticed, each period, hating myself for not intervening. No pranks happened in the locker room, thankfully. At least, I didn't think so. Mike and Gael's lockers were in different rows. And I knew to keep to myself while dressing to avoid the epithets thrown at friendless boys with supposedly wandering eyes.

During a free period I went to the library. I stopped short when I saw Gael sitting by himself at a table, his head propped up by one hand while the other tapped a pen against an open notebook. It looked like he was writing an English composition.

My heart pounded. I walked to another table, hoping he had not seen me. But I sat down, fidgeting at the thought that another opportunity to talk to him without classmates watching would not arise. But what would I say? How would I build a connection? How could I show him that I was like him? Another Mexican.

I wrote down a series of sentences to introduce myself in Spanish. I crossed out more grammatically complex ones for simpler, more direct ones, sentences that I knew were correct. I got up and walked toward Gael, repeating the words in my head. With each step I imagined how his face would light up upon hearing his native tongue spoken by a classmate, the surprise on his face when he learned of my Mexican heritage. And I saw flashes of me introducing Gael to my band friends, how we would envelope him into our group and have countless weekend misfit adventures.

"Hola," I said, straining to pronounce everything as natively as possible. "*My name is Brett. We have gym together. How are you?*"

Gael's brow furrowed. "Mira, fresita, no soy un chango con quien puedes practicar tu español."

It was an answer I was not expecting, a response not from textbooks, a string of words only snippets of which I could catch. I chuckled nervously. "Perdón?"

He scoffed. Gael stood up abruptly and swiped his books off his desk. He nearly body checked me on his way out of the library.

*

I saw Gael in gym for another week or so afterward. I avoided eye contact but I still felt the resentment in his glare. Even though I knew his bitterness was directed at the other students too, I hated being grouped with them in his eyes. A part of me wanted to correct the situation, to defend myself, to show Gael that I was different. I was Mexican after all. Why wouldn't we become friends? But each time I mustered up the courage to talk to him again I shrank back, recalling the sting of his rejection. A rejection that denied my *latinidad.* But a rejection that paled in comparison to what he felt. Did I even deserve Gael's friendship? My attempts to befriend him were out of a selfish need for identity. He was a means to an end, and not an end to be respected; a conduit and not a person.

And then one day Coach Z did not call out Gael's name. He was not in class that day, either. Of course the students speculated with Mike as their head conspiracy theorist. I later found out while eavesdropping on a guidance counselor's conversation with another teacher that Gael's family had moved away suddenly with no warning other than a terse phone call. For the rest of the semester when Coach Z read roll call I flinched each time he was supposed to say his name.

DNA

David Radavich

I am proud
of my African past.

Deep in my body,
hidden in the blood
of migration, suffering,
grace, sunrise.

I have learned
the language of genes.

It speaks of
moving out and apart,
two feet on earth,
two eyes, two hands,
a face beyond fear.

I have kept going.
I am here.

You know my dark heart,
its beautiful shadow,
this mind that acknowledges
all beginnings in one
continent that sings in sun.

Speak to me, proud blood.

COATS OF DIRT

Evelyn Burd

He walks next to her quietly, nervously. The condom in his pocket is burning into his thigh. He knows that he should be home by now, that his mom will be up waiting for him, but he's young and believes that if this doesn't happen tonight… he doesn't know what. That it'll never happen, he'll never be invited to another party, that the girl he'll fall in love with the first year of college will end up with someone else, that he'll be stuck living with his mom forever.

He doesn't think the girl next to him is more or less nervous than he is, but he can't really tell. They've known each other since the fall, and it's now spring, so that's about… seven months. Of course, their banter in physics keeps him awake, and she always makes him feel warm. But he doesn't really know her well enough to read her. He was definitely caught off guard when she asked him if he wanted to meet and told him to bring a condom.

They're getting deeper into Riverside Park, and it feels weird to be heading somewhere so public, somewhere his mom used to take him after school, but neither of them knew where else to go. It's so hard to imagine the future of this, when he'll bring lovers home with him to stay in his room and no one will even break a stride in their speech because it'll be so normal and everyone around him will be doing it too. That feels so far off, the days when he won't be able to remember what it was like to have to sneak around. The days when he'll be laughing at these moments with his mom, when he'll be telling this story to someone tucked into the crease of his shoulder in bed and his eyes will be mostly closed and he'll say more details than he thought he remembered.

But for now, he's got the ring-shaped second-degree burn on his thigh and a girl whose curls he could write poems about, if he let himself get nearly as whimsical and hyperbolic as he does when someone at the lunch table asks who's still a virgin.

What do you think about here? she says. It might be the most private place in the whole city.

He laughs. Of course, he can still see the water, and New Jersey, but it *is* tucked under the pathway. Maybe it'll be over quickly and then they can both go home. Not that he doesn't want to enjoy it, and not that he thinks he won't, but it'll be better after the first time anyways, right?

They fumble and he feels awkward and thinks how she looks completely different here in the dim park light than she does in their 8 a.m. class, where she barely stays awake and books are always falling out of her bag. He has never worried about how he looks in front of her because she always looks about the same, but he becomes very conscious of his nails accumulating dirt where he curls his fingers under his palms on either side of her head.

They kiss, and he feels himself touching her in most places and wonders if she wore a skirt to make things easier. He knows he's getting hard and they'll be able to do this, but he feels so scrambled, almost sick to his stomach. They've made out a couple of times at other friends' houses, but he's never touched much of her bare skin before. And he won't tonight, either. He knows he can slip himself out of his jeans and up her skirt, and the architecture of it will work for them. For a second, he thinks about his parents and all the ways they must have done it, and then he feels himself flush, feels the heat travel through his body and churn his stomach more. He doesn't want to picture his mom, the breasts that fed him, the watchful but comforting eyes that try to guide him. He tries to purge her from his mind and focus on the task at hand. He reminds himself it's worth it, the awkwardness of this moment, the difficulty he'll have looking into this girl's eyes on Monday, because he'll never have to do it like this again. There's a reason people like to say, "Let's get this over with."

And he does. So quickly, actually, that he's embarrassed. But at least now he knows he'll move out of his parent's house at the appropriate age, and he won't die alone. He pushes himself up on his knees, removes the condom, and pulls his pants back up. She reaches for her underwear somewhere in the leaves, and they stand up. He knows he shouldn't leave the condom on the ground, but he doesn't know if he can bear carrying it next to her all the way to a trash can.

As they walk out of the park, she starts humming a song. He asks her what it is, mostly to be courteous and indicate that he cares, and less so because he actually does. She can't remember, but she'll send it to him later when she does, when she can't fall asleep. Not because she's not a virgin anymore and that knowledge is sinking in, but because she's been an insomniac since high school started, because the stress just won't leave her alone. He'll listen to the first couple seconds of the song the second after she sends it to him, because he'll be up too, until he hears the line "the first time always cuts the deepest," and he'll think, briefly, of the shallow dent they made in the park dirt.

They split up at the 72nd street metro station. There's a dry leaf in her hair, but he can't bring himself to tell her. On the walk home, he's clothed in a coat of dirt himself, one he doesn't see and doesn't run down through the shower drain. He's glad for the city air, the familiar sounds, the feeling of being alone but not isolated in place and time. The lights in the deli on his block are harsh, but he regains his focus after about ten steps and starts to feel himself drifting as he pulls himself up the three flights of stairs to his front door.

His mom is waiting up for him. Somehow, he had forgotten that she would be. He doesn't stop to say anything to her. He just passes her and walks down the hall to his room. After he starts the tap and pulls the knob to change the course of the water, he hears his mother's bedroom door close quietly, and he goes back to marveling at his own independence.

He sleeps like a baby that night. He doesn't have nightmares about his future, or what might befall him. He doesn't know yet that when he gets to college, many of his friends will not have had sex. Doesn't know that he'll be sad and embarrassed when he thinks of this night in a year. Not because it happened, but because of how he didn't think about the girl, didn't think about what he wanted, or much of anything at all, really. His mother lies awake, on her back, staring at the ceiling instead, and these thoughts will not relent. She thinks about her own childhood, the free reign with which she was raised and the lack of observation which she was given. She hopes, when her son thinks back on his childhood, it will not be with feelings of regret and anger. And she doesn't need to worry, because he wakes up the next morning, not particularly interested in having sex ever again.

THE AFRICAN SEES SNOW AND SHIVERS

Obinna Chilekezi

The world in a deep freezer, very cold
After days of heat and summer burnt
Here am I an African, I walk, I freeze, I shake but smile
A newcomer knowing that the world needs this cold too
To further live, so that we can live too

I stand here a newcomer to snow, staring at this wintry love

Do I claim to love this cold, not at all, but great love for the
grayish sights?
Hope this scenes be transported back home but without this
killing cold
So my kinsmen too share in this shock of walking in earth's
deep freezer too
As here the day walks in a cold smile from dawn to dusk
And the lonely newcomer befriends more loneliness across the
streets

I stand here a newcomer to snow, staring at this wintry love

Yes here the day smiles with a cold smile
The African on a strange journey dreams of nothing but home
"Take me home, to Africa, our land of perpetual sunshine"
As the bald-head man walks along the wintry street, receiving
strange slaps of snow
"Take me back home, to Africa, to our land where the sun

never fails to show its teeth each day"

I stand here a newcomer to snow, staring at this wintry love

Here the weather is a god, especially during winter
Here the weather is part of the daily devotions,
The people draw their timetables of to go or not to go with the
weather in mind
Here in this cold weather, a lonely newcomer dreams of his sun
The lonely newcomer shivers as snow falls, buzzing, blowing
very ray cold sirens across.

MY MOUTH IS A WAR ZONE —

Kaylianne Chaffee

a gravesite, rows
of marble tombstones jutting
through earth-coffin-earth

a casket, and we
are all pall-bearers
for a box of bared teeths
cloth-covered to say
                       "I am
trying not to be a death threat"

I know my mouth is a game of
one bullet in the chamber
one hand on the trigger

— a kiss. a kiss. a kiss.

BIOGRAPHIES

MICAELA ACCARDI-KROWN is an emerging author from the Los Angeles area who writes to escape this world, if only for a moment. Her writing tackles themes of childhood, grief, and magic. She hopes when you read her work it will be like opening your favorite old-looking, best-smelling book...touching the yellowed pages, and quietly falling into a dream. She received her B.A. in Literature and Creative Writing from the University of California, Santa Cruz, and has been published in several literary magazines and anthologies. She is currently the Publicity Manager for Golden Foothills Press based in Pasadena, CA.

CARRIE ALBERT is a multifaceted artist and poet. Drawings, collage, comics, photographs and visual art/poem pairings have been published and featured in numerous journals, among these: *ink, sweat & tears, cahoodaloodaling, Grey Sparrow, The Monarch Review, qarrtsiluni, Gargoyle, Penhead Press,* and *Chestnut Review.* She lives in Seattle, where she is a featured artist at Four Corners Art.

KARYNA ASLANOVA is a multimedia artist, director, and photographer based in England. Karyna's art photography projects often use other-worldly imagery to reflect modern social issues, with a vague but familiar base note perceptible through a haze of the strange and incongruous.

ROBERT BEAR spent fifteen years as a video editor and producer, where he wrote scripts for television and corporate communications almost daily. He is an Emmy-winning editor with numerous Telly and Addy awards to his name across two decades of work. Throughout all the media he has worked on, there has been one consistent belief: that story rises above all, that content is king. He has been married to his high school sweetheart for 30 years, and they share two children. He works currently as a high school film teacher while attending Lindenwood University.

Photo reporter and visual artist **GUILHERME BERGAMINI** is Brazilian and has a degree in Journalism. For more than two decades, he has been developing projects with photography and the various narrative possibilities that art offers. The artist's works dialogue between memory and political-social criticism. He believes in photography as an aesthetic potential and a transforming agent of society. Awarded in national and international competitions, Guilherme Bergamini participated in group shows in 41 countries.

Some people play video games, or the cello; **ELIZABETH BOQUET** plays poetry. When she's not doing that, she teaches English, translates FR-EN, and chairs The Pernessy Poetry Workshops in Lausanne, Switzerland, where she lives with her husband, a watchmaker. Over thirty of her poems have appeared in various literary journals and magazines and her first poetry collection, *GALOSHES*, was published in October 2020. Naomi Shihab Nye awarded her a Geneva Writers' Literary Prize (2nd place) in 2017, and her work has been featured by National Poetry Writing Month twice. Visit her page, elizabethboquet.com

At present time, **KATERYNA BORTSOVA** is a painter-graphic artist with BFA in graphic arts and MFA. Works of Kateryna's took part in many international exhibitions (Taiwan, Moscow, Munich, Spain, Italy, USA etc.). Also, she won a silver medal in the category "realism" in her participation in "Factory of visual art," New York, USA and 2015 Emirates Skywards Art of Travel competition, Dubai, United Arab Emirates.

Kateryna is always open for commission and you can view her work on Instagram: @katerynabortsova, or on her website: bortsova6.wix.com/bortsova.

PAUL BUFIS has had a varied background in academia, concrete contracting, and IT consulting. His poetry has received commendation from the Chester H. Jones Foundation, been nominated for the Pushcart Prize, and has been published in a variety of literary publications and anthologies. His work has appeared in *Southern Poetry Review*, *River Styx*, *Rhino*, and *Permafrost*, among others. Some recent work is included or forthcoming in *The Poeming Pigeon*, *The Remembered Arts Journal*, an anthology *For Expecting Mothers*, and *pacific*REVIEW.

EVELYN BURD is a writer from Austin, Texas and is finishing her undergraduate degree in literature at the University of Chicago. She enjoys reading current literature, short stories, and the classics. She is particularly interested in how we come to love people, what draws the line between a best friend and a lover, and how language and language learning impacts our relationships. She will be starting her MFA in Fiction at Columbia University School of the Arts in the fall.

KAYLIANNE CHAFFEE is a poet, violinist, synesthete, and professional mess-maker from San Diego. They are currently finishing their bachelor's in English with a creative writing certificate at San Diego State University. When they aren't writing, they play plenty of music and paint on objects that were never meant to be canvases.

OBINNA CHILEKEZI is a Nigerian poet whose works have appeared in anthologies such as *Twenty Nigerian Writers*, *For Ken For Nigeria*, etc. His poems have appeared in journals and serials like *Rake*, *Better than the Starbuck*, *Daily Times*, etc. His insurance text won the African Insurance Book Award in 2016.

JUAN CORTEZ is in the first year of his PhD program at the University of Wisconsin-Milwaukee. He earned his master's at the University of San Francisco and his bachelor's at DePauw University. He is a poet, a picky reader, and an avid traveler. A guiding quote that Juan lives by comes from Richard Hugo: "You owe reality nothing and the truth about your feelings everything." When not writing or reading, you can find Juan out for a stroll through nature, taking in his surroundings, lost in thought.

RC DEWINTER's poetry is widely anthologized, notably in *Uno: A Poetry Anthology* (Xlibris, April 2002), *New York City Haiku* (Universe/NY Times, February /2017), *Coffin Bell Two* (Coffin Bell, March 2020), *Winter Anthology: Healing Felines and Femmes* (Other Worldly Women Press, December 2020), *Now We Heal: An Anthology of Hope* (Wellworth Publishing, December 2020), and in print in *2River, Adelaide, Door Is A Jar, Event Magazine, Gargoyle Magazine, Genre Urban Arts, Gravitas, Kansas City Voices, Meat For Tea: The Valley Review, the minnesota review, Night Picnic Journal, Prairie Schooner, Reality Break Press, Southword* among others and in numerous online literary journals.

M.A. DUBBS is an award-winning Mexican-American and LGBTQ+ poet and fiction writer from the Hoosier state. Her first collection, *Aerodynamic Drag: Poetry and Short Fiction*, came out in early 2021.

JANICE FRIED is a mixed media artist currently working on fabric collage. She graduated with a BFA in illustration from Parsons School of Design in NYC and she has spent many years walking the fine line between illustration and fine arts. Her work has appeared in many publications and she has exhibited her work in and around the NY Metro area.

MADI GIOVINA writes poems and stories. She is a co-editor for *Backslash Lit*, submissions coordinator for *What Are Birds? Journal* and the founder of Perennial Press. Madi lives in Philadelphia with her feisty cat, Shrimp. You can find her on Instagram @ cyberinsecurity.

MATT L. HALL is an award-winning fiction author originally from Austin, TX. He holds a B.A. in English from the University of Massachusetts. His work explores themes of redemption, family, and perseverance despite unhealed trauma.

ALI HEADLEY was born, raised, and now resides in Nebraska. Currently, her work ranges from painting, photography, and digital art. After Ali's corporate job as a graphic designer, she has re-discovered her need for other forms of art, focusing on painting.

L. KARDON is a queer parent and poet residing in Philadelphia, PA. Lily's work can be found in *Wizards in Space*, *The Rubbertop Review*, *Diaspora Baby Literary Magazine* and more. Follow Lily on Instagram at @lilykcontent for more.

POLCHATE (JAM) KRAPRAYOON is a Bangkok native and works for an intergovernmental agency in Tokyo. He received a master's from the University of Oxford and a bachelor's at the LSE. His work has been featured in *Glass: A Journal of Poetry*, *Portland Review*, *Split Rock Review* and is forthcoming in *Whale Road Review* and the *Beloit Poetry Journal*. His poems have been nominated for the Best of the Net and the Pushcart Prize.

NICK LAMIA is an award-winning artist whose work, despite its non-objective appearance, is based on real, lived experience—often involving outdoor adventures in the mountains and on the ocean. His artworks are metaphoric representations of the overlap of the natural world with built society. Lamia is a Guggenheim Fellow and has had residencies at Wave Hill, The MacDowell Colony, the Robert Blackburn Print Workshop and the Triangle Artists Association. He lives and works in New York City.

MASHA LISAK is a poet and non-profit professional living in Oakland, CA. Her poetry has appeared or is forthcoming in *Sycamore Review*, *Eunoia Review*, *Written Here*, *DWELL* and elsewhere. She was the 2018 Editor-in-Chief of the journal of the Community of Writers at Sq**w Valley. A Napa Valley Writers Conference fellow, she was selected for the AWP Writer-to-Writer mentorship program in 2019.

CIERA LLOYD doesn't know a world without writing. In May of 2021, she will attain her BFA in Creative Writing, minor in English, and certificate in publishing from UNCW. After graduating, she will begin studying at City, University of London in September to earn her MFA in Creative Writing. She, and her other published work, can be found on Instagram @ciera.lloyd.

Painting is **MARIO LOPRETE**'s first love: an important, pure love. Creating a painting, starting from the spasmodic research of a concept with which he wants to send and transmit a message, is the base of his painting. The sculpture is his lover, his artistic betrayal to the painting. That voluptuous and sensual lover that gives him different emotions, that touches prohibited cords… For his Concrete Sculptures, he uses his personal clothing. Throughout some artistic process, in which he uses plaster, resin and cement, he transforms them into artwork to hang. His memory, his DNA, remain concreted inside, transforming the viewer of his artwork into a type of post-modern archeologist that studies his work as if they were urban artifacts.

AIMEE LOWENSTERN is a twenty-two-year-old poet living in Nevada. She has cerebral palsy and is fond of glitter. Her work can be found in several literary journals, including *Soliloquies Anthology* and *The Gateway Review*.

JEFFREY H. MACLACHLAN also has recent work in *New Ohio Review*, *The Meadow*, *Santa Clara Review*, among others. He is a Senior Lecturer of Literature at Georgia College & State University.

KEILY V. MALDONADO is an afro-Latinx artist living and working in Los Angeles. She is a graduate from UCLA with a BA in Fine Arts. Maldonado delves into the exploration of mental illness, generational trauma, and the complexities of the human condition. Keily's work is multifaceted in the way that it interlaces a variety of mediums and color schemes to create a space for associative thought and emotional sensibility. The fantastical characters she creates in her nightmarish imaginary worlds grasp at the illusionary concepts they believe love to be. Loss, love, and suffering are thematic concepts that enforce a space for empathy.

ANDRES ENRIQUE MENDOZA is a self-taught poet and essayist. Growing up in Los Angeles, early childhood meant facing the realities of marginalization and gang warfare. Moving to Oregon in his later years, continuing the lifestyle, at age 17, he faced several Measure 11 charges and was sentenced to serve over six years in the Oregon prison system. Recognizing the role marginalization played in his incarceration, he has decided, through writing about his personal experiences, to humanize those living in marginalized communities. His work has appeared in *Thebeatwithin*, the *Words Unlocked 2016 Anthology*, and is currently working on publishing a zine.

TOMAS NIETO is a writer and educator from San Diego, California. An alum of Las Dos Brujas and VONA/Voices, his work has appeared in *Solstice Literary Magazine*, *The Rumpus*, *Mud Season Review*, and others.

ERIC ODYNOCKI is a teacher and writer from New York. His work is often inspired by his experience as a first-generation

American of Mexican, Ukrainian, and Jewish descent. Eric's work has been published in *Gordon Square Review*, *Cold Mountain Review*, *American Poetry Journal*, *PANK*, *Magma Poetry*, and elsewhere.

EMILY JOY OOMEN is a journalist and multimedia poet from the Pacific Northwest. Her work has been featured in BBC, the Athens International Video Poetry Festival, *Vice*, *Buzzfeed*, and many other publications. She has a B.A. in English from the University of Washington and helps curate videos for Button Poetry. You can find her on Instagram @poetic_espresso and on Twitter @emilyjoyoomen.

MATTY PENNER is an artist, writer, and mental health advocate. He graduated from SDSU with an MFA in creative writing. He's currently finishing his memoir entitled "Hide Your Shoes." He's been published in *Confusion Magazine* and the *German Magazine BrettKollegen* twice. You can find his art at TheRollAwayArt.com or on his Instagram @TheRollAway. Ten percent of all proceeds are donated to the International Bipolar Foundation.

ERNST PERDRIEL was born in Montreal (Quebec, Canada). He is a multi-field artist (visual art, photography, writing -French), designer and horticulturist.

He has participated in solo and group exhibitions in visual arts since 1995. The artist uses mosaics, collages, landscaping, and photography to talk about our complex era. Perdriel has contributed in numerous publications since 1992 as a writer, illustrator, artist, photographer and in self-publishing. His works have appeared in *Sunspot Literary Journal*, *Meat for Tea: The Valley Review*, *Kolaj Magazine*, *Into the Void*, *The Healing Muse*, *Iris Literary Journal*, *3Elements Literary Review* and others. Learn more at ernstperdriel.com

Among **DAVID RADAVICH**'s recent poetry collections are two epics, *America Bound* (2007) and *America Abroad* (2019), as well as *Middle-East Mezze* (2011) and *The Countries We Live In* (2014). His plays have been performed across the U.S. and in Europe. Radavich's forthcoming books are *Here's Plenty* (Cervena Barva Press) and *Unter der Sonne: German Poems* (Deutscher Lyric Verlag).

EMILY RANKIN was born in Riverside, California and attended university in Abilene, Texas, where she received a BFA in 2011. Her body of work ranges from Graphic Design and Scenic Painting to collaborative performances with Verstehen, an interactive series which incorporates live painting, sound, and electronics. She is currently based in New Mexico. Visit her page, eerankinart.com

ERIC RAWSON lives and teaches in Southern California. His work has appeared in *Agni*, *Commonweal*, *Slate*, *Ploughshares*, *Iowa Review*, and numerous other periodicals. His most recent book is *Banana Republic* (2020).

VANESSA RODRIGUEZ graduated from San Diego State University in May of 2020 with a Master of Arts in English and an emphasis in Comparative Literature. Writing acts as her escape and her therapy, and she hopes to indulge in it for as long as she can. Her poetry has appeared in the *Aztec Literary Review* and her short fiction has been published in *Catfish Creek* and *This is Writing*, the latter winning first prize in the Creative Writing Short Story Contest in 2018. She loves music, vintage furniture, and watching the same three TV shows over and over again.

GREGORY FRANCIS ROYSE II grew up in Yosemite National Park. At an early age, Gregory began painting and drawing under the guidance of his grandmother who is an art teacher and oil painter. Gregory moved into photography and studied under notable Yosemite photographer, Nancy Robins, from an early age. His photography has been shown in the Ansel Adams Gallery and in various galleries as part of the Sierra Art Trails. In recent years, Gregory's work has taken on a more digital and graphic design focus; this has offered him the opportunity to explore both photography and traditional art.

DORIS E. RUBIO is a 24-year-old Colombiana/Chicana living in San Diego, CA, who enjoys punk rock, poetry, patacones and pan dulce. Her last publication was "questions for henry rollins' unibrow," for *Freezeray Poetry 2019*. She is an English major at San Diego State University.

RACHELE SALVINI is an Italian woman based in the U.S., where she is doing a PhD in English and Creative Writing at Oklahoma State University. She writes both in English and Italian. Her translations and work in English have been published or are forthcoming in *Lunch Ticket*, *American Book Review*, *Necessary Fiction*, *Modern Poetry in Translation*, and others. One of her essays won the 2020 edition of the Stirling Spoon contest 'Identity in America.'

LABDHI SHAH is a self-taught artist from India, currently based in Atlanta. She received her B.A. in Economics & Psychology from Fergusson College, Pune, India, and her M.A. in Psychology from Indira Gandhi National Open University, and is certified in Arts-Based Therapy from BAPU Trust, Pune.

Her effort as an artist is to share her faith in the capacity of love, and to accept the uniqueness of every human being irrespective of race, color, gender, and culture. She works with a variety of media including watercolor, acrylic, charcoal, and ink, and enjoys the uniqueness of each medium.

TAKWA (TEE) SHARIF is a Somali-American writer and social worker. She loves education and is passionate about social justice and the arts. Currently, she is a social worker in Ogden, Utah. She also loves to spend time with her partner and two dogs.

LESHUN SMITH was born and raised on the southeast side of Chicago, Illinois. His community of Grand Crossing can be described as predominantly black people who are among the working poor, but with intersections of poverty, violence, drugs, and gangs. This made it easy for talents like writing to be eclipsed. At 41, LeShun has now spent over half his life in prison. What was once eclipsed has now resurfaced and taken up agency. Writing has become his portal to reclamation, eventual liberation, and immortalization. With Northwestern as a springboard, he is able to reach new heights.

You can connect with him via LeShunSmith#R06121@ connectnetwork.com (NPEP) Northwestern Prison Education Program.

COCO SPENCER is a mixed-media artist with an emphasis in analogue collage. She was born in a car on Highway 99 in Merced, California. She is now based in Chicago and enjoys collaboration. Her work can be found @cocozpencer.

SHANNON STEINKAMP grew up in the Appalachian foothills of Northern Georgia. She currently resides in Milledgeville, Georgia with her husband, Caleb, and their two children, Joshua and Elisabeth. She teaches English at a public high school and hopes to inspire students in the same way she was inspired.

TRAVIS STEPHENS is a tugboat captain who resides with his family in California. A University of Wisconsin-Eau Claire alumni, recent credits include: *Gyroscope Review*, *2River*, *Sheila-Na-Gig*, *GRIFFEL*, *Offcourse*, *Crosswinds Poetry Journal*, *Gravitas* and *The Dead Mule School of Southern Literature*. His book of poetry, *skeeter bit & still drunk*, will be published by Finishing Line Press in 2022. Visit him at: zolothstephenswrites.com

DALE STROMBERG grew up not far from Sacramento before moving to Tokyo, where he had a brief music career. Now he lives near Kuala Lumpur and makes ends meet as an editor and translator. His work has been published here and there.

KATLIN MARISOL SWEENEY is a PhD candidate in the Department of English at The Ohio State University who specializes in U.S. Latinx studies and popular culture. Her research interests include Latina representation and production on the Internet, prison media, and DIY cultures. She was central coordinator of SOL-CON: The Brown, Black, and Indigenous Comix Expo and an executive team leader with the Latinx Space for Enrichment and Research (LASER) from 2019-2021. Her work can be found in *The Routledge Companion to Gender and Sexuality in Comic Book Studies* (Routledge, 2020) and *Cultural Studies in the Digital Age* (Hyperbole Books, 2021).

MCKENNA THEMM graduated summa cum laude with her B.A. in Literature and Writing from CSUSM. She is currently an MFA in Creative Writing: Poetry student at SDSU. Her poems have been published by the *San Diego Union-Tribune*, *JMWW*, *Bryant Literary Review*, and *The Stray Branch*. She is writing her first full-length collection of poems, based on the life and work of Vincent van Gogh. She is the managing editor at the *Los Angeles Review*, a Content Strategist at Circa Interactive, the MFA Director's Assistant at SDSU, and a Teaching Associate at SDSU.

JEANETTE C. VIGLIOTTI is a doctoral candidate at Virginia Commonwealth University's Media Art Text program. Her academic and creative work investigates identity in digital and material spaces.

KWONG KWOK WAI, WALTER is intrigued by the motif of human existence and ponders over it in the context of people's memories and history. He finds this would be best to present in symbols and abstractions as it provides possibilities and uncertainty. In search of his cultural origin and identity, he also published three full-length novels and one short story collection.

ALLISON WHITTENBERG is a Philly native who has a global perspective. If she wasn't an author, she'd be a private detective or a jazz singer. Her novels include *Sweet Thang, Hollywood and Maine, Life is Fine, Tutored, The Carnival of Reality*, and *The Sane Asylum*. Her plays have been performed at Interact Theatre, The Spruce Hill Theatre, The Festival of Wrights, and The Playwright's Center.

MARCIE WOLF-HUBBARD received her B.A. in Studio Art from the University of Maryland and studied Fine Art & Illustration at the Maryland Institute, College of Art. "Drawing is my connection to the world. Encaustic painting provides a play of light, with a surface you want to touch. I add, and take away, sometimes making the painting more of a sculptural form.

Working with students has also fueled me in this time of sadness and uncertainty. Art has lifted anxiety and inspired us all to continue creating."

Marcie is a Teaching Artist in the DMV (DC/MD/VA.)

THANK YOU FOR READING

To learn about future submission opportunities,
visit pacrev.submittable.com/submit or email
info.pacrev@gmail.com

Special Offer to Readers of pacREV 2021! Order back issues of pacificREVIEW at the special authors's discount rate! Go to **pacificreview.sdsu.edu** and use the links at the bottom of the page. Our last 7 years offered for a song!

http://pacificreview.sdsu.edu